Chapman 76: Sp

THE WOMEN'S FORUM: Women

Cover
Caroline Hunter

Illustrations
Caroline Hunter, Tash MacLeod, Deborah Cumming, Carola Gordon

ISBN 0 906772 59 1 ISSN 0308-2695

CHAPMAN

4 Broughton Place, Edinburgh EH1 3RX, Scotland
Tel 031-557 2207 Fax 031-556 9565

Submissions:

Chapman welcomes submissions of poetry, fiction and critical articles provided they are accompanied by a stamped addressed envelope or International Reply coupons

Subscriptions:

	Personal		Institutional	
	1 year	2 years	1 year	2 years
UK	£12	£23	£15	£28
Overseas	£15/$28	£28/$54	£19/$36	£36/$65

Subsidised by the Scottish Arts Council

Printed by Mayfair Printers, Print House, William Street, Sunderland, Tyne & Wear

The Saucers and the Shark

Alison Armstrong

Tonight the lamp may strike. It's a cobra with a head like the sun – like *looking into* the sun. You won't let me switch it off but I can't turn my back because of what it might do.

Why do you keep an anglepoise here? It isn't a bedroom light – it belongs in a study. (We don't have a study or a private room. Extra rooms are expensive, you said, when you took me flat-hunting). So in our case the cobra should live in a box, until we can buy a big house with spare rooms. I've seen the house I want, in town. It's Victorian, with peeling paint and a creepy dreamy garden, and I'll buy it when I'm strong again. I used to be very strong.

I'd get my strength back if I bought a proper bedside lamp. I've seen the one I want in Debenhams – its base looks like a blue eggshell and it has a shade in blue to match. I asked you to buy me it for my birthday last year, but you forgot. At least I think you forgot.

You've said we won't have much spare cash this year as we're going on holiday. Did we decide on Malta? Or Cyprus? You were dithering between the two before you came to bed and I didn't catch the one we plumped for. I'll be happy as long as I can swim. In the water I can get away from people as most of them don't swim out as far as I can.

Roll on summer, and Malta, or Cyprus – or wherever you are, holiday. Let's bake in that cobra the sun.

Baking's your sort of holiday. You can lie without a care in the world, turning as black as a barbecued sausage. When we were in Greece last year, I stood up to baste you and the sand burned my feet. I got suntan oil everywhere – on my clothes, my hair, even my book.

That's what you bought me last birthday! A book! And the exercise tape to go with it. The book's interesting as it describes how the author lived on cigarettes and cheesecake and sicked the cheesecake up again because she felt guilty. That was in the 1960s, and now, aged fifty, she looks great in a leotard. I look awful in those things. And if I wear a bikini, all my fat makes rolls above my pants. White, bready rolls. Doughball.

I'll slim for our holiday this year. I'll listen to that tape. If I had a job I'd eat less, but there's nothing for me to do. I failed teacher training because my eye contact was bad – that's what they *said*, anyway. It doesn't bother me, but if I'd passed, I'd have some money. I'd buy one of those lamps in Debenhams, then I'd buy some clothes and have a good haircut. I've never had decent clothes, and when I was younger I told everybody that clothes didn't matter. I suppose I was like Esther in *The Bell Jar*, doing fine but hurtling towards chaos… Nobody else at school had read *The Bell Jar*. My anorexic friend in the Sixth Year wanted to be Sue Ellen from *Dallas*, and she's done well. She now drives a white company car and doesn't speak to me any more.

I wish I had some money.

In Sixth Year, I wouldn't have been scared of a lamp. Then, I was a dynamo, a bomb – but now I'm only fluff and feathers, soaked with tears and as heavy as a lead weight. There must be a machine for turning such rubbish back into power. If I wasn't going to Maltacyprus this year, I'd go to painting classes, but I'm not much good. Perhaps the machine works by thinking you're good, even when you're not.

The other night I was reading a magazine and some inserts fell out and hit the floor. The shock – I was in on my own – nearly gave me a heart attack. Before I moved in with you I'd go anywhere, do anything... Now I'm frightened of paper.

Help me if you can I'm feeling down

That song bounces along so cheerfully, you don't notice how dismal it is until you really *listen.* When we were in Greece the cocktail bar played Beatles songs all the time. You said you didn't notice, but I listen to the music wherever I go. 'Help' made me sad, and Rikky – remember Rikky from the hotel? – said that if I didn't cheer up he wouldn't buy me a Blue Hawaiian.

Rikky was a character, wasn't he? He was a plumber from South London and I bet he'll be a millionaire before he's thirty. He said he'd been in jail more than he'd been in school, and he was still pretty wild. You didn't like him very much, but you didn't like avoiding him either. His absence made us dull.

I think you envied his fascism, but you couldn't bring yourself to say so. Rikky disliked Blacks, vegetarians, gypsies, moustaches, lesbians, cauliflower... He never explained why, and this began to annoy me. After one or two cocktails, I let him know.

(Drink lets me spin on a different axis. I don't move like the world expects me to...

...is that why you don't keep drink in the house?)

If I didn't shout at Rikky, I was very loud. You kept telling me to shut up but I didn't. At one point Rikky and I hated each other and I thought he was going to hit me. Even then I didn't stop. I didn't win but I didn't lose, either. After the argument he bought me the Blue Hawaiian, which came with a swizzle stick like a shark. The shark's my Debating Trophy. It came back here with me and it's in my box along with my collection of saucers you don't like. When I buy that Victorian house, I'll have the saucers and the shark on the mantelpiece, which you won't like at all.

Since Greece, you've twisted the light to make it shine straight into my eyes. You say you can't sleep in the dark, but we don't have to have this cobra. Any light would do.

I don't think you'll ever get rid of the cobra. Like everything else in this flat – the bed, the couch, the video recorder – it's working for you.

We bought most of the furniture together. You asked me what I liked and I pointed and said "yes". I liked the things in the shops but when they came here I couldn't take them in. I still can't – they could still be in the shops, in their plastic wrappers. The saucers and the shark are different, but I can't sit on them or use them to tape a television programme. They're

junk, really. Useless. Connected to nothing worthwhile.

That cobra watches me so you can sleep. I've become good at showing nothing – my hands are above the quilt, and my head… well, all the words and meanings floating around there make sense if you're good at reading tealeaves. I don't think you are. You like seeing furniture, not the dark, because – I think – the infinite disturbs you.

Fancy a swim?

I wonder if I'll find a Rikky on Maltacyprus. You brought posh-looking brochures home, so it isn't likely. In Greece there were plenty of white maggoty Brits floating in the hotel pool, who went "whee!" when they fell off their airbeds. I had to push maggots and airbeds out of the way when I did my twenty lengths each morning. Without those lengths the fortnight would have crumbled, as routine's more important on holiday than in real life.

Rikky couldn't believe how much I swam. I told him I could swim forty, sixty, even a hundred lengths in the pool as long as I didn't get bored. Boredom's the killer.

Tea leaves. When there's something to aim for, all those mental tea leaves floating about, pull together and make a *real* pattern.

If Rikky hadn't asked me I wouldn't have done it.

It happened when we went on the island trip. There was no shade on the beach and people who were already peeled raw lay out and boasted of the tan they'd take back to Glasgow or Manchester. They saw my sunblock and thought I was mad, but I know you want me to dry up, like a slug.

At lunchtime I waited in the Barbiequeue next to girls who looked as if a morsel of kebab would leave an ugly lump. (Where do thin women hide food before it's digested?) When it was my turn a gust of wind blew under my paper plate and sent oiled salad and meat juices down my front. You and Ricky were nearby. Rikky laughed but you were annoyed because I was showing you up. You told me to clean myself in the sea.

(I don't think you remember that incident. It was a small thing that wouldn't have happened if I'd been strong.)

I waded into the sea, up to my neck. Water's the best place to be when something goes wrong. I balanced on one big toe and discovered I could go round and round, using my toe as a pivot. To do this well I had to face away from the beach and forget about the food and the exercise tape. When I carved big circles in the sea, I changed axes without being drunk. I stared across the bay, where a cliff rose from the water, as white and as smooth as a ski slope. To get to that cliff I'd have to cross deep blue icy water, with perhaps jellyfish and sharks...

"Fancy a swim?" Rikky's hands rested on my back. It wasn't a sexual touch. In a swimsuit I'm no Jerry Hall. He touched me to pass on some of his daring, and I said yes.

We struck out. I swam breast stroke (the only stroke I know) and Rikky swam a mixture of breast stroke and the crawl. When we left, you were playing in the shallows with a beach ball.

I'll keep to the shallows in Maltacyprus. I don't want to swim those depths again. When we were about half way across, we seemed to be swimming and swimming and going nowhere, and I thought, what if I forget how to swim? I would have died if I hadn't fixed on the ski slope, which made all the tea leaves come together and force me along. I had the same *propelled* feeling at school whenever I got A grades.

I reached the ski slope first. Its small chalky stones were painful on bare feet. Worse, the sun tried to burn us into shadows and we'd no lotion, but we couldn't go back without swarming to the top and exhausting those itchy little demons in our guts. Once at the top, we looked across the bay and watched a flea circus of beach party games. I couldn't identify *you.*

We started to burn very quickly, so we half-slid, half-scrambled down the ski slope. We found a stunted tree almost at the water's edge and we sat beneath it and talked. Rikky told me about prison and I told him about teaching. "I couldn't handle your type", I confessed. He looked surprised, then laughed. I don't believe you, that laugh said. You're a better swimmer than I am.

...I now think... he pitied me. No one can respect a woman who gets salad down her front. After the holiday I brought this respect home and put it in my box, but it's gone stale. I dare say the plastic shark looks tacky now. *Your* things, on the other hand, get stronger. They suck juices. The bedclothes roll us up together and the bugs that even clean people have, go from me to sheet to you then round again and again, feeding. *We* don't matter. The lamp will dry me up if the bugs don't eat me first.

You're snoring gently. If you were awake I wouldn't know how to speak this and make it sound right. I had the same feeling when Rikky and I swam back; I didn't have to explain winning. How do *you* know what it feels like, when you don't lose? You were lying on your back, eyes closed, headphones on, and Rikky's girlfriend said she'd been oiling you and changing your cassettes. She was used to Rikky doing stupid things, she added.

"What if something had bitten you?" you asked when you found out. You weren't cross. You weren't anything.

You didn't seriously think "what if?" In your philosophy, things either happen or they don't. If I could think like you, I'd be happy. I'd be happy if, for once, I could just clear all the rubbish away...

I must get rid of that box. The saucers and the shark are just rubbish and if they go, the tear-soaked fluff and feathers will go too. Burdens. The machine works if you are *light*.

Thank you for buying me the exercise tape. I'll use it now, as soon as I've cleared out that box.

It's not easy, to kick free of these sheets. I don't want to wake you, as I'm doing all this myself. The trouble is crossing the bedroom floor with that cobra trained on me. The bulb is turning in its hood, like a slow head. I can't avoid it, but I haven't far to go. The box is in the cupboard in the hall, and once I'm through the bedroom door, I'm clear...

I'll turn on the stove and have molten shark for my supper. Then after I've splintered those old saucers, I'll put the tape on. *Stretch* two three four five six seven eight. I'll be the most beautiful girl in Maltacyprus.

But *why*? Why the necessity at a quarter to two?

"What are you doing?" Muffled, spoken through the quilt.

"Just getting a glass of water."

Selftraitor.

"Bring a bottle of juice when you come back."

You're lying as well, pretending everything is normal when you've had the light trained on me since Greece. Only our little sane bits connect, leaving everything important unsaid. I can't do it tonight. Now you're awake I'd have to explain what I was doing and it would all come out crazy when it isn't crazy at all.

I'm going back to bed. Once I've killed the saucers and the shark I won't leave sweaty invisible footprints on your rug. I won't be fat and heavy any more...

"Thought you were going for a drink."

"Changed my mind."

Humph.

The bed nearly collapses under my weight. I'm surprised you've said nothing straight out, as your exercise-tape hint hasn't worked.

The cobra is back in position, as if it never moved. You mutter: "Try and get to sleep."

Nothing's happened to make me tired, although I'd stand a chance in the dark.

"Can I switch the light off?"

"No."

You turn your back, and contract into the warm nest you've made for yourself. Disobedience is out of the question. It just *is*. No explanations.

Silly cow, as Rikky – who I swam a mile with – would say. You silly – stupid – *cow*.

The cobra will never go away if I just lie here. Turning off a light is an easy thing to do – you just click.

...There it goes. Easy.

Not like waiting for your voice, in this breathing-filled darkness I've made.

Alison Armstrong

Kathleen Jones

Alone at night

Alone now in the old house
I lock doors, fasten windows
and close the curtains to keep out fear.

There is nothing outside but sheep
standing patiently in dark fields
keeping watch for winter foxes.

The trees toss restlessly in the garth
talking amongst themselves.
There is nothing outside but the dark.

Inside the fire burns optimistically;
its flame a brand to thrust
in the eyes of ravening wolves.

I am not used to silence,
the quiet conversations of sheep
the breath of trees, fox cry.

Sometimes in the night
I wake and feel the silence and the dark
filling the sockets of my skull.

An emphasis of want

(for Christina Rossetti)

There were no birthdays
in that narrow house
whose silence, curtained windows
and the senile mutterings of three old women
muffled the words
that crawled painfully from her pen.

Not surprising that she wrote of absence.
Two lovers and a sister dead,
Elizabeth Siddal's suicide,
Lucy Madox Brown's consumption,
Dante Gabriel thrust violently out of life
by laudanum and whisky –
and not one Pre-Raphaelite
at the funeral.

Not much like the beginning –
the dreaming virgin painted by her brother,
Hunt's radiant Christ,
Madox Brown and Swinburne at the door,
Millais and Morris and Burne Jones
bringing embroidered silks and tapestries.

Too shy to meet the Brownings
and the Poet Laureate
she stayed at home
creating goblins in the notebook
Ruskin disapproved of –
"...so full of quaintness and offence...
no publisher would take them."

Italian sensuality corseted in black,
a tongue tied by formality,
concealed her passionate poetry,
erotic fruit, burned letters,
the home for prostitutes in Highgate.

Till, broken by the stress of flesh and faith,
the worship of a sacrificial God
who wanted everything,
she lay, eaten by cancer, terrified
she had not sacrificed enough –
had kept back just one metaphor
too many, screamed
to watch hell's creatures
obscenely cavorting on her bed
and no one there but the maid
to stand between her
and the death she waited for.

The fell gate

Hung between stone monoliths
framing a postcard view
it marked the limits of our territory.

At six I swung, forbidden
wedging my toe caps in the sheep wire
nailed to the wood, watching
my father and his circling dogs
driving them in across
the nape of the fell
ready to hitch and drag it open
at his whistle.

Taller, I climbed it
racing for the ridge
through fox-coloured tussock grass
and nesting curlews
avoiding the green mires
deep enough to drag a horse down;
warned against abandoned mines,
houses with eyeless lintels
and the ghost of Sworley
wife-murderer,
who hanged himself in the barn.

Now, with the farm empty
the gate dislocated from its hinges
and the fields tussocking over
with rush and gorse, I pass
through its open cromlech
into a tourist's landscape.
Still able to feel
the hitch and drag of it
in my hands,
strong enough to pull
a whole life down.

Fiona Wilson

Conversion

Is white marble. Is a cool,
architectural light. Is the clinking
of glass fish from the bazaar,
blue, clear, amber.

Battiya pours one long,
gold finger of iced tea,
tempers it with honey.
She has become graceful too suddenly.

Next door, her husband, the poet,
struggles to describe the hole
God left, having created
the sky. He sees it

like a twister, in his mind's
eye. Battiya places cornflowers
in a tall crystal vase.
They take up the morning

with their steadfast blue.

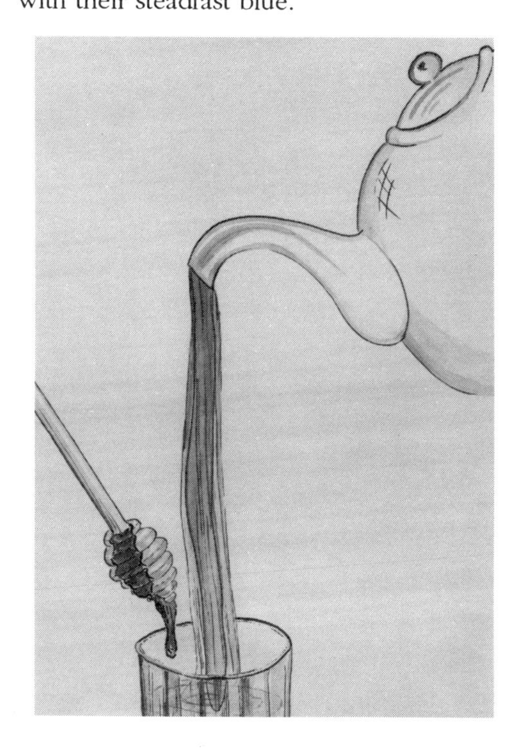

Inland

The impression of gulls at twilight:
soft phosphorescence, the vagueness
of wings. A poem
that hovers and hovers
till no longing on earth can name it,
still less, summon with words
its presence.

Letters from Eilean nam Ban

At Fionnphort
Bathed in a tub scrubbed
Clean as a bone
And grounded four-square
On obdurate Empire paws.

Still
Through the small window I saw
Slew of land-
Scape and knot. Heard
Your singing, your exotic

Male Voice
And thrill threading up
My spine, the colonising impulse,
And I, island, breasts, knees,
Rising out of water in

Small lines
Of body, hip
Glanced to knee, anvil
Of shoulder blade rocking
In socket, fibula and tibia,

Hand
To heart, it's true
That in your absence
Desire seems both clearer
And further

Away
To the vanishing point,
Your fool's gold,
You don't know
My language, or even

The last chapter
Content at last
In the abrupt charge
Of rain.

Pirouette

What we have:
a little rust,
the cool hands of clocks
meeting on the edge of each hour.
It is an instant of touch –
so intimate in its own distraction
one can hardly tell
if it's the starlings
needling the electric air
or simply the long signature
of your body against mine.
Sweet. As you leave, you call behind
that even this was found wanting.
I say there is want
and then want. Breast, shoe,
some food, a kiss.
One day it'll be you,
just you,
pirouetting in an empty room.

Woman carrying a broken stereo

(After 'Mujer Angel' by Graciela Iturbide)

It's a good bell, her body. She moves it in a single, held
note, swaying the blunt stereo
like incense. The first revelation
is of wholeness (her walk scything the nippled flowers);
the second is the smell of new-turned earth. A strange visitor
and certainly, something, somewhere,
is chiming.

So where does this voice come from, this voice
reciting that what breaks is what chimes, what chimes
the recurrent pang of a gangling wire? I have heard this
again and again. I will not hear it any more.
Simply, I am a woman looking at a woman
whose body bells the landscape.

Did you think the flowers were red? A silver print
is witness only to the noise of shape.
The mountains move off like planets. Scattered trees rise up
as men that were sleeping. There are blisters on her fingers
and instruction in her shoulders. The desert is a veil.
Bridegroomed it lies, a continent
before her bleeding feet.

"She's a musical lassie"
Women in Scottish musical history

Ann McKay

Read most musicological tomes and you would be forgiven for thinking that women throughout history have been totally unmusical, so rarely do they get a mention as classical musicians or composers. Scottish musical history, superficially, is no exception, though women do feature more strongly in our traditional music culture, both as performers and composers. Scottish classical music history has been so little researched or written about, but a glance at those milestones which do exist – Farmer's *A History of Music in Scotland* (1947), David Johnson's *Music and Society in Lowland Scotland in the Eighteenth Century* (1972) and John Purser's *Scotland's Music* (1992) – will show that the musical arts of the gentler sex have not passed those authors by completely unnoticed.

Music history is generally written by men about a male-orientated art form. But when one compares this art form to others – visual arts, and literature – it is strange to notice that whereas the art world could produce, promote and even praise an Angelica Kaufman, Madame Vigée le Brun, a Joan Eardley, or the literary world a Jane Austen, a Charlotte Brontë, and in Scotland the Gaelic bardesses like Mary MacLeod and Sileas MacDonald, the few women composers we know of are dismissed as amateurs. Clara Schumann deferred to her husband's supposedly superior compositional skills; Gustav Mahler forbade his wife Alma to compose – until she threatened to leave him; Felix Mendelssohn's compositional talents took priority over sister Fanny's – and so on.

To understand why women musicians – especially composers – have fared so badly in the past, we need first to take a general look at social conditions in Western Europe of the eighteenth and nineteenth centuries in which classical music was able to flourish. In order to become a leading professional musician, the neophyte required three things: an advanced musical education; full-time employment as a performer in an orchestra or choir, as a Kapellmeister or teacher; and opportunities to travel – to hear and study the contemporary music of the day and to advance a concert career. For composers the additional requirement – the luxury of time to compose – could be afforded only through subsidy in the form of a rich aristocratic patron, a publisher, or an individual or corporate commission.

Given these prerequisites, how could women stand a chance? Musical education was still primarily the preserve of an all-male church – at primary, secondary and tertiary level – and the only women to receive an education were those of the higher levels of society who could be educated at home or in a convent. Strangely, well-bred young women of the period were required to acquire the art of music if nothing else, but their practice of it went no further than the living room.

Full-time employment as a musician for a woman was unthinkable except for the operatic prima donnas. Many performing and teaching posts were in church – and therefore male – hands. At a social level, the status of performing musicians was somewhat akin to that of actors, so that for a woman who had acquired all the training and education necessary to becoming a fine musician, to practice this profession would have meant a demeaning step down the social ladder.

Travel opportunities for women? Except in the company of supervising male relatives, husbands, or theatrical agents, these were non-existent – though female opera singers toured at home and in Europe to maintain careers. The idea of a young woman composer going off to study with a great teacher in a foreign country was unthinkable.

And time to compose? Though romanticised by some, the composer was still seen by many as menial, a craftsman rather than an artist. And patronage for a woman composer? Again unthinkable. Publishers too have a lot to answer for. In the 18th and 19th centuries they would only take on a composer and his catalogue if he had a proven track record: they had their profits to think of.

Music is fundamentally a social activity – even solo vocal writing usually requires an accompaniment. Because women composers saw little chance of having public performance of their works, they tended to write for fellow-women likewise constrained by social conventions – keyboard music, songs. For example, in eighteenth century Scotland the recorder, flute, violin and cello were played only by gentlemen; the gamba and keyboard instruments by both sexes, though the piano became an increasingly female prerogative during the course of the century; and the cittern was played only by women. This reflects the contemporary society: whilst men went out to work and met each other, women remained at home. "Male" instruments are sociable ones that can form chamber groups, orchestras, while "female" ones are independent, harmonically self-supporting. The gamba could be played as "division" viol playing, a style in which the playing of chords made the instrument harmonically self-sufficient. To quote David Johnson: "A male/female distinction also held in singing, for ladies typically sang solos in their own homes, while gentlemen sang together away from home – glees in the tavern, or choruses of Handel's oratorios in the concert hall. For women, music-making was an individual activity; for men, it was a group activity."

But what of those women musicians who *were* active in Scotland before the twentieth century? The nineteenth century throws up a surprising number of women who were highly successful, even famous in their own day, but have since been largely ignored. The information available on their lives and careers is scant and patchy: those sources which do exist seem to suggest that they had no lasting impact on the musical world. Or did they? Our résumé will begin with those who made their name as performers. For this information I am greatly indebted to Henry Farmer, and the various editions of *Grove's Dictionary of Music and Musicians.*

Mary Ann Paton (1802–64) was "an exquisite soprano with a wonderful compass". Her father was writing-master at the High School of Edinburgh, and the family was musically gifted. Mary Ann was already learning the harp, piano and violin at the age of four. At eight she made her first solo appearance in Edinburgh as a singer and violinist, playing a concerto by Viotti. She also published several compositions. Her reputation as a singer was secured by her debut as Susanna in Mozart's *The Marriage of Figaro* at London's Haymarket in 1822. For two decades she was at the top of her profession in recital, oratorio and opera, performing at both Covent Garden and Drury Lane. In 1824 she married Lord William Pitt Lennox, a younger son of the 4th Duke of Richmond, continuing to perform under her maiden name. The marriage was later dissolved and she married another singer, Joseph Wood, with whom she toured the United States on three occasions. Her sisters were also opera singers – Isabella at Drury Lane, and Eliza at the Haymarket – but I can find out nothing about them.

Eliza Inverarity (1813–1846) was an Edinburgh-born soprano who made her debut at the age of 16. In 1836 she married the bass Charles T Martyn, with whom she appeared in operatic performances throughout Britain, and also in the United States, where her most notable role was apparently in Beethoven's *Fidelio.*

Elizabeth Masson (1806–65) became best-known as a composer and teacher, though she trained as a singer in London and Italy and appeared regularly in recitals in London over a twelve year career, during which she "revived forgotten airs by Purcell, Handel, Pergolesi, Gluck, Mozart etc." She retired from singing to teach and compose, and wrote many songs to words by such poets as Scott, Byron, Adelaide Proctor *et cetera*, and edited a series called *Original Jacobite Songs* (1839). Her teaching methods produced a book of *Vocal Exercises* (published in London in 1855) and *Songs for the Classical Vocalist.* With Mary Sarah Steele, she was the founder in 1838 of the Royal Society of Female Musicians – which in 1866 amalgamated with the Royal Society of Musicians of Great Britain.

Robena Anna Laidlaw (1819–1901) was born in Bretton, Yorkshire of Scottish parentage, but was educated at her aunt's school in Edinburgh, and had her earliest piano lessons there from a Robert Müller. In 1830 her family moved to Koenigsberg, Germany, where her future was decided and after three or four years of study she appeared in concert in Berlin, to great acclaim. By 1834 she was studying in London under Herz, and played at Paginini's farewell concert (1834), and at other concerts in Berlin (1836), and at the Leipzig Gewandhaus (1837). Shortly afterwards she was the dedicatee of Schumann's *Fantasiestücke* Op.12. A lengthy tour of Prussia, Russia and Austria followed and an appointment as pianist to the Queen of Hanover. In 1840 she returned to settle in London, marrying, in 1855 at the comparatively advanced age of 36, a fellow Scot, a Mr Thomson, after which, to quote the history books, she "retired". What became of this internationally famous pianist is apparently of no further interest to musicologists. One can but wonder what retirement entailed for a woman who had led such an interesting and itinerant career!

Euphrosyne Parepa-Rosa (1836–74) was born in Edinburgh, the daughter of a Wallachian boyard, Baron de Bayescu, and an English singer Elizabeth Seguin. Her father died when she was young, and her mother brought up the child, her destiny on the stage already decided. She made her operatic debut at the age of 16 in Malta, and in the course of her life appeared in operas, oratorios, and in the concert room throughout Europe. At the end of 1865 she went to America for a concert tour with Carl Rosa and married him there in 1867. In the States they established their famous opera company, in which Euphrosyne was principal singer. Returning to England in 1871 she sang Donna Anna in Mozart's *Don Giovanni* and Norma in Bellini's opera at Covent Garden, and toured to Cairo and Düsseldorf. Her health, however, was rapidly declining, and she died in 1874. In his wife's honour, Carl Rosa founded the Parepa-Rosa Scholarship at the Royal Academy of Music.

Helen Hopekirk is another enigmatic figure, sadly lacking from the pages of most history books, though a short biography of her by American musicologist Constance Huntington Hall (1954) has recently come to light. Born in Edinburgh in 1856 she came from a most musical family, but it was Helen who was apparently chosen by her father to be prepared for a life as a virtuoso pianist. She studied the piano with George Liechtenstein (a Hungarian pianist resident in Edinburgh), and by the age of seventeen was performing concertos – including Beethoven's 'Emperor' – with the Edinburgh Amateur Orchestral Society. She also studied composition and accompanied the violin-playing of Sir Alexander C Mackenzie. Her piano studies continued at the Leipzig Conservatory (1876–78), and her debut took place in Leipzig at a Gewandhaus concert in 1878, when she played Chopin's Concerto in F minor. The following year she played a concerto at the Crystal Palace Concerts under the baton of Sir August Manns. During the next three and a half years Hopekirk performed throughout England and Scotland, giving premieres of several works. She met many famous musicians – including Clara Schumann, Edvard Grieg, Franz Xavier Scharwenka, and Anton Rubinstein (of whose performances she later wrote "No player has ever had the same power over me or seemed to me so giant-like.") In 1882 she married a Scottish music critic and business man, William Wilson. They enjoyed a long and by all accounts unusually happy married life: Wilson was most sympathetic to his wife's career, and wholeheartedly devoted his resources to her advancement – more or less giving up his own career in business. Helen kept her maiden name, becoming known as Madame Helen Hopekirk. They had no children.

In 1883 the couple moved to the United States. There Hopekirk had tremendous success as a soloist, notably at the Boston Symphony Concerts and the Philadelphia Festival. Critics commented on the quality, range, and size of her repertoire "probably larger than any other pianist save Rubinstein", remarking too that she always played from memory – apparently not a universal practice at the time. And her delightful, intelligent, generous, and unaffected personality won friends everywhere.

In 1886 Hopekirk decided – and I find this most surprising of such a well-established pianist – that she wished to study again – with Liszt. On her way to meet Liszt in Bayreuth in July 1886 she learned of his death. So in March 1887 she and Wilson moved to Vienna where she took piano lessons with Leschetizky, who spoke of her as "the finest woman musician I have ever known" – and composition with Nawratil. She resumed her playing career in 1889, including a performance of Bach's Triple Concerto in A minor with the Vienna Philharmonic Orchestra under Richter.

In 1890 the Wilsons were back in the States, but in 1892 they moved to Paris so that Helen could concentrate on composing. In November 1894 she premiered her *Konzertstück* for piano and orchestra with the Scottish Orchestra in Edinburgh and Dundee under Georg Henschel. 1895 found the Wilsons living in London, where in January 1887 William was badly injured in a traffic accident. Helen now needed a dependable income from her profession, and later that year they settled permanently in Boston where Helen taught at the New England Conservatory. The rest of her life was spent teaching (from 1901 privately in Brookline), performing and composing. She was much loved by her pupils, of whom she was very demanding. She gave numerous US premieres and pioneered the music of many contemporary composers in the States – especially French and British. She wrote several orchestral works (premiered by the Boston Pops Orchestra), works for piano and orchestra, two sonatas for violin and piano, and a large number of solo piano works. Her reputation as a composer in her own day rested largely on her output of some 100 songs (many to words by Burns and Fiona MacLeod). William Wilson died in 1926; Hopekirk continued to perform until a month before her 83rd birthday, and taught up to her death in November 1945 at the age of 89.

Hopekirk's attitude towards other women musicians was somewhat ambivalent. She wanted to be judged not as a women composer or a woman pianist but as an individual making a contribution. But in 1901 she wrote a curious letter to the American magazine *Etude* concerning piano teachers. She believed that teaching ability was found equally in men and women but she opposed "the thoughtless plunging into teaching by women that is so prevalent". She went on:

> In this country there is a perfect mania to become a teacher of some sort or other among people who, in Europe, would not feel themselves demeaned by doing housework well. Many girls would be much better employed and more comfortable keeping houses orderly and nicely – say for other women who through their work lack the time for personal supervision – than in giving cheap, bad piano lessons and swelling the ranks of victimizers of our much-abused piano.

At the same time she was an ardent suffragist, and greatly respected other woman musicians and composers. Hopekirk's story is a fascinating one, unusual but maybe not unique.

Jessie McNiven McLachlan (1866–1916) was a soprano whose singing of Highland songs in Gaelic endeared her to Scots everywhere. On several occasions she sang at the concerts of the Gaelic Society on London where she so intrigued Queen Victoria that she was commanded to appear in Balmoral in 1892. Better known was another soprano, of Scottish parentage but born in India – Margaret McIntyre. She studied in London and made her debut in 1888 in Covent Garden, singing Micaela in *Carmen*. Her success continued and she sang such major roles at Covent

Garden as Mathilde in Rossini's *Gulielmo Tell* , and Marguerite in both Boito's and Gounod's *Faust.* Her career took her all over the UK – including festivals at Leeds, Birmingham, and at the Glasgow Choral Union concerts in 1890. She was the first Rebecca in Sullivan's *Ivanhoe* and sang Senta in *The Flying Dutchman* at Covent Garden (1892). McIntyre also appeared in St Petersburg and Moscow (Elizabeth in *Tannhäuser*).

Last of this group of distinguished Scottish singers comes the soprano Mary Garden (1874–1967), probably the only name still remembered in Scotland today. Born in Aberdeen in 1877, she spent her youth in America, and in 1895 went to Paris to study. She made her debut in Paris as Louise in Charpentier's opera, and then appeared regularly in seasons in London and Paris, and in 1907 in New York as Thaïs in Massenet's opera. She sang at the Manhattan Opera House until 1910, and then the Chicago Opera House, where apparently for one season, 1921–22 she was its Manager/ Director – when she was responsible for the creation of Prokofiev's *The Love of Three Oranges.* Garden had a remarkable number of roles to her credit, and indeed was responsible for the creation of several now-famous characters. The best known of these was Mélisande in Debussy's *Pelléas et Mélisande*, which was probably her most successful role.

So in the 19th century Scotland attracted attention through the skills of her vocalists – only to be expected in a land where song was everywhere – and pianists. Many of these women were singing at the top opera houses of the day, with other famous singers, playing with the leading orchestras in the famous halls, under distinguished conductors. They studied at home and abroad, and were able to undertake overseas tours in the company of the most famous musicians of their day. How could they manage to do so? Most came from well-heeled families, often already associated with professional music-making, who thus also understood the greater appreciation of musicians accorded by the publics of America and Europe. The success of our pianists is explained by the presence of the piano in most well-to-do houses, where its study was considered a necessary social accomplishment. Presbyterian attitudes severely limited the use of the church organ, which in any case was certainly not considered an instrument for ladies. Orchestral instrumentalists were not plentiful – probably due to lack of encouragement and Church disdain for mere "fiddlers" and "pipers". There were plenty of amateur music societies in the Scottish cities, and several of theses evolved into more professional outfits. But many of these were still closed to women.

What of the composers? Helen Hopekirk we have already mentioned. Isabella Mary Scott (1786–1838) is curtly dismissed by Henry Farmer. Edinburgh-born, she "gained immediate favour with her ballad Loch-na-gar... because it had sentimental national attraction". Alicia Ann Spottiswoode (1810–1900), eldest daughter of John Spottiswoode married Lord John Montague-Douglas Scott (son of the fourth Duke of Buccleuch d.1860) in 1836, and after her father's death in 1870 resumed her maiden name – not a usual gesture for the 1870s. She is chiefly remembered as a composer of Scottish songs – an "amateur" according to the books – including 'Annie

Laurie' which was first published anonymously in 1838. She is also credited as being the composer or arranger of 'The Banks of Loch Lomond'.

Women have played a very important role in preserving and collecting Scotland's folk music heritage. Lucy Broadwood (d.1929), granddaughter of John Broadwood the piano maker, himself a Scot, was one of the enthusiastic founder-members of the English Folksong Society (1898), and became its Secretary (1904–08). She collected all over Britain, but "largely in the Highlands". Anne Geddes Gilchrist (1863–?) was a collector of Gaelic material in Skye and the Isle of Man.

Francis Tolmie (1840–1926) was possibly the greatest of the collectors, and acknowledged as such in her own lifetime. She was another, like Lucy Broadwood, of those "twentieth century... maiden aunts of independent means..." (Frank Howes). She wrote numerous articles on songs and lore, most famously in No.16 of the Folk Song Society's *Folk Song Journal*. This issue, edited by Lucy Broadwood, contains some 105 items from Tolmie's large collection of songs. An excellent book on Francis Tolmie's fascinating life, times and her songs is *The Old Songs of Skye – Francis Tolmie and her Circle* by Edith Bassin. Readers wishing to discover more should turn to this, but the brief facts are as follows.

Born in 1840 in the MacLeod country of Skye, Francis Tolmie was decended on both sides of her family from distinguished Hebridean families. Her interest in the Gaelic tradition began early: as a child she begged her mother to teach her the old songs. Later she learned Irish Gaelic and was evidently familiar with Welsh and Manx.

Her father died when she was only five. She was one of the younger members of a large family, and in her late teens and early twenties lived in the Manse of Bracadale, on the west of Skye, where her brother was parish minister. It was a wonderful place and the perfect atmosphere for the development of her interest in the Gaelic tradition. Among friends of the family were Alexander Carmichael, collector and editor of *Carmina Gadelica* and Thomas Constable, an Edinburgh printer and publisher.

University education for women was still a long way off but, aged seventeen, Tolmie spent a winter in Edinburgh attending classes in English language and literature, and taking private lessons in French, German, Italian and music. She was a gifted musician, singing and playing the piano.

Her folksong collecting began in earnest on her return to Skye. Living at Bracadale she was asked by Miss MacLeod of MacLeod to distribute wool among the local women in connection with a home knitting scheme. This involved long distances on foot, and her mother insisted that Francis should have an escort on her walks across the moors. Rather than a girl of her own age Francis chose elderly women – two in particular, Effie Ross and "Little" Margaret Gillies. On the walks they sang songs, and recounted lore and stories of ancient ways. From the beginning Tolmie was encouraged by Alexander Carmichael and others to write down all she heard and learned – the music she notated in sol-fa. She kept all her notes.

During the 1860s Tolmie was governess for some years to Thomas Constable's two young daughters. The Constables' home was a comfortable and cultured one. It was there that she came across John Francis Campbell of Islay's newly-published *West Highland Tales*, in which she found, to her delight, "the fireside tales known to us all". But all the traditional learning she had gathered was to remain in the background for many years. Between 1866 and 1873 Tolmie was back in Skye with her mother, tutoring young family members and friends, and continuing her research. But she was missing the intellectual stimulation and cultural discourse she had found in Edinburgh. Though the universities were still closed to women, university professors were holding lectures for women – in Edinburgh, for example, on subjects including English Literature, Mental Philosophy, Experimental Physics and Botany. These lectures continued to be over-subscribed until University classrooms were finally opened to women.

In Cambridge at the same time there were the beginnings of the women's colleges, Newham and Girton. It was to Merton Hall (Newham was being built) that Tolmie, then aged 33, went for two terms in 1873–74, as one of the earliest women students. It is not known why she only stayed a short time – financial circumstances could well have been the reason – but events took another turn for her. In 1874 she went to visit a friend, Miss Harriette Rigbye, then over sixty and an amateur artist of independent means, and one of John Ruskin's circle at Coniston in the Lake District. Rigbye only lived in the Lakes during the summer: every winter she spent in Italy, the south of France or Switzerland. For twenty years she was accompanied in these travels by Francis Tolmie. Tolmie's position with Miss Rigbye may well have been the envy of many. Her duties appear to have been entirely social – she seems to have been required simply to "be in attendance". In effect she was a companion. It was a friendly arrangement and she received no salary, but all her expenses were paid. Very little information remains of the twenty years Tolmie spent in England: in a letter to Lucy Broadwood she dismisses them as "...a dream, a wonderland of beauty and kindness..."

In 1895 Tolmie joined her sister in Oban, but by 1900 was living again in Edinburgh. That year Alexander Carmichael published the first two volumes of *Carmina Gadelica*. Visiting the Carmichaels in Taynuilt, Tolmie met Dr George Henderson, the famous Celtic scholar and author, who, on hearing her sing some of the songs and learning of the existence of her manuscripts, encouraged her to expand and tidy up the collection. It was through him that finally in 1907 she was put in contact with the English Folksong Society, who were eventually to take custody of her collection. And in 1911 the famous Volume 16 was published – two years after the first volume of the famous *Songs of the Hebrides* of Marjory Kennedy-Fraser. Kennedy-Fraser knew Tolmie well and, indeed, obtained much of her material from her. Tolmie remained in Edinburgh until 1915, when she returned to Skye to spend her last days at Dunvegan, separated from her birthplace Uiginish by a narrow sea loch.

Marjory Kennedy-Fraser was the most distinguished of the eleven children of the great Scottish singer, David Kennedy. The whole family was musical, and at one time or another all the children assisted their father in his concerts and entertainments as accompanists or singers. David spent some 26 years touring the world – Australia, New Zealand, South Africa, India, Canada, United States and Europe – until his death in Canada in 1886. Marjory was born in Perth in 1857 and her father was her first singing teacher. She was also a pianist, and at the age of 12 became her father's accompanist. She completed her singing studies in Milan and Paris, and then continued to tour with her father until his death. Her marriage in 1887 to Alec Fraser, a mathematician and schoolmaster in Glasgow, did not take place until after her father's death, and sadly her husband did not live long after the marriage, though they had a son, David and a daughter, Patuffa. After Alec's death in 1890, Marjory continued her career, teaching piano and singing in Edinburgh, and giving lecture-recitals on aspects of song – probably, in part, through financial need.

Kennedy-Fraser's interest in folksong was first prompted by a collection of Breton Songs, and in 1905 she paid her first visit to the Outer Hebrides. She began to collect folksong material (a few of her archive recordings are held in Edinburgh University Library) and study it. She published her own arrangements, and brought the repertoire into the public domain through her lecture-recitals, where she was accompanied on the clarsach by her daughter Patuffa, and on the piano by her sister Margaret (who married the distinguished English pianist and composer Tobias Matthay, teacher of such pianists as Myra Hess and Harriet Cohen). Because Kennedy-Fraser was first and foremost a musician and not a scholar her academic research, printed in the *Laws and Interpretations of Hebridean Song* and *Lowland Scots Song*, has been lambasted as unscientific and inaccurate. The arrangements, well-suited to the voice but criticised as "too free", she defended on the grounds that the songs varied according to time, place and singer. Modern purists shy away from her piano accompaniments, but she was doing exactly the same as her contemporaries Bartók and Kodály in Hungary. She also composed a suite for cello and piano, *Songs of the Hebrides*. Kennedy-Fraser died in Edinburgh in 1930.

This tradition of folksong collecting has been carried on by women today – notably Margaret Fay Shaw in the 1950s, and those who have passed through the School of Scottish Studies at Edinburgh University.

Before we move onto the Scottish women who have helped to shape musical life in the latter part of this century, let us briefly evaluate the contribution made by their 19th century sisters. I have concentrated on biographical detail and social circumstances rather than, in the case of the composers, compositional styles. Much of their music is unobtainable, many of these compositions have disappeared, and assessment of musical quality would have to be made, most unscientifically, on hearsay.

Possibly the greatest distinctly Scottish barrier preventing more women in the 19th and early 20th centuries becoming professional musicians were the prevailing strict Presbyterian social attitudes. These firmly kept women of all classes in their place – in their homes, factories, or churches. While a woman could become a society hostess, skilled in the essential arts of piano playing and singing, she was not expected to practice these arts anywhere but the drawing room, or as the century progressed, in choral singing. Presbyterian attitudes towards entertainments limited paid employment opportunities for all musicians, though the situation greatly improved as the century progressed. They kept down the number of theatres; music in churches was anathema; there was no professional orchestra until 1874, and no full-time orchestra (the BBC SSO) until 1935; no professional opera company; and the societies arranging concerts of chamber music and vocal recitals (an increasing number from 1830), tended to favour visiting, preferably foreign artists. The growth of amateur choral and orchestral societies from the 1840s built audiences and led to a greater number of concerts. Teaching was a fairly profitable profession with the growth of the middle-classes, their drawing-room pianos and their genteel daughters. The Socialist movement too was active in its encouragement of education and of participation in artistic activity. The Glasgow Athenaeum was established at the turn of the century, providing employment for some and training for others. But like their male counterparts, women wishing to make a career as a solo performer or composer usually had to leave Scotland, as exemplified by many of those mentioned above.

Given these circumstances it is surprising that Scotland could produce a Robena Anna Laidlaw, a Helen Hopekirk, a Mary Garden. These were only the most prominent women in their field, the ones who had been offered and grasped the opportunities: there were many more for whom the opportunity never arose, or whose careers have gone uncharted by the historians. These women were famous – internationally famous – in their day, and, particularly as teachers, influential. Those whose family backgrounds lay in the music profession seem to have fared better. True, composers have always struggled for recognition (normally only gained when the composer is dead!), but while McEwen, MacCunn, Drysdale, Mackenzie and Wallace were all greatly respected in their day and are remembered still, Helen Hopekirk, with probably a greater international reputation, has slipped from memory.

But social and cultural conditions have changed greatly since the days of Helen Hopekirk. Today music colleges and universities are turning out female musicians in great number. With more job opportunities they are filling our orchestras, teaching in our schools and conservatories, forming their own ensembles, making international careers. For the top women singers and instrumental soloists the demands remain as high as they ever were – constant international travel to fulfil prestigious engagements is now complicated by the pressures of the recording industry (and often the requirement to be the perfect wife and mother too). Role models are there and new ones being continually created. More women are working in the music profession in Scotland than ever before; in full-time and freelance capacities; in all areas of classical, folk, pop, jazz, light, and world musics; as performers, composers, arrangers and teachers; and in management.

I do not intend to discuss the many women performers working in Scotland over the past fifty years, save to say that they set great examples, and have opened up great opportunities for their successors. I think particularly of the women who have played in the professional orchestras, worked on stage, and taught. Thanks to them we have a generation which can boast an Evelyn Glennie, a Marie McLaughlin, a Linda Finnie.

But for women composers the story is not happy. It has become easier to be a woman and a composer, but it is still difficult. Women have had a remarkable impact on contemporary music in Scotland over the past thirty years. Such women as Thea Musgrave, Janet Beat, and more recently Judith Weir and Sally Beamish provide excellent role models for the increasing number of women now studying composition at Glasgow and Edinburgh Universities or the Royal Scottish Academy of Music and Drama – where, at the moment, there are no women composers teaching full-time. Indeed the reputations of Musgrave and Weir (both of whom have publishers – Novello and Chester Music) in particular have achieved greater international significance than most of their male counterparts, and Beamish too is now attracting major British commissions.

Changes in the publishing world have benefited women composers, though there is as yet no serious contemporary music publishing firm in Scotland. Once publishers admitted that new music was neither popular nor commercial (the back catalogues of classical composers are their income generators) they could take risks with young and women composers. But then they unwittingly discriminate with remarks like "but we already have a woman composer in our catalogue..."

In 1992 the BBC's London Promenade Concerts featured one woman composer (Elena Firsova) amongst 103 men, and in 1993 one woman (Weir) out of 100 composers. This is also reflected at music festivals everywhere. But is positive discrimination, carrying with it the suspicion of compromised musical standards, the answer? Probably not. Weir will not talk about the problem. Beamish says: "Composers need a sort of entrepreneurial personality. Women don't often like to do this kind of thing, thinking it's unfeminine. Composing is unique. You need interpreters and players, and if you're not working to commissions you have to persuade people to play your music. Perhaps being a well-brought up, educated, middle-class woman also makes it difficult to go out and sell yourself!" Compared with the many men composers who adopt a very convincing hard sell persona, I can think of no women who do the same. Part of the problem is that composition and performance are often divorced in Western classical music. Building a network of performers is one answer; having a publisher is another. Of course some composers are simply writing music that nobody wants to hear, or music that is not good enough for public professional performance. But there is excellent music by women composers that is rarely, sometimes never, heard. The same is true for men composers, so that discrimination against women is not the issue here. Yet in this age of the CD precious little music by either Weir or Musgrave is commercially available compared with that of their British male counterparts. Perhaps positive promotion and marketing *is* the only answer.

Born in Midlothian in 1928 Thea Musgrave studied at Edinburgh University and privately with Hans Gal before going to Paris in 1950 for four years to work with the redoubtable Nadia Boulanger. She returned to England to compose and teach, but since 1970 has been resident in the United States where her husband Peter Marks is now General Director and Conductor of the Virginia Opera Association. Musgrave's output covers a wide range of genres, from full-length operas to simple unaccompanied choral motets, from orchestral works to brass band music, from chamber music to teaching pieces. She has received many prestigious commissions: in Britain, among them several for the BBC including *Cantata for a Summer's Day* (1954) and the Viola Concerto (1973); for the Feeney Trust the Concerto for Orchestra (1967); for the Royal Philharmonic Society *Peripeteia* (1981); for Scottish Opera *Mary, Queen of Scots* (1977/86), for the Royal Opera House *The Voice of Ariadne* (1974), and for the Cheltenham Festival the Second Piano Sonata. In the USA major commissioners include the Koussevitsky Foundation, and Virginia Opera. Most recently Musgrave composed an overture *The Rainbow* for the opening of the Glasgow Royal Concert Hall in 1990, and future premieres include a percussion concerto for Evelyn Glennie in 1994, and the opera *Simon Bolivar* in the States in 1995.

Judith Weir writes of Musgrave: "40 years' worth of published work reveals Thea Musgrave to be one of the most industriously inventive of post-World War II composers. A capacity for constant self-renewal combined with a shrewd awareness of what is currently happening in musical style have produced an unusually varied and ever-developing series of works." The early works from her time spent in Paris are lyrical and tonal, and mainly vocal with a very individual choice of texts – like Maurice Lindsay's poems for *A Suite o' Bairnsangs* (1953). In the years after her return from Paris her style became more chromatic, her forms more abstract – closer to the continental musical language of the period. During the 1960s, while she was exploring serial techniques, Musgrave discovered the dynamic which has inspired her music ever since: the idea of "dramatic-abstract" music (her terminology) in which dramatic processes are discovered and enacted in abstract (i.e. non-programmatic) musical settings. This involves techniques like asynchronous music where each part is notated but need not be exactly coordinated with the others; and theatrical tendencies like the physical movement of players on and around the stage. The dramatic-abstract music is best represented by a highly original series of concertos – including the Concerto for Orchestra, and concertos for clarinet, horn and viola. In them the accompanying orchestra becomes a collection of individual and smaller groups, equally capable of inner division and subversion as unisons. The soloists lead instrumental sections away from the main tempo and musical direction of the rest of orchestra, creating a sense of interference from the soloists and their allies. The dramatic situation is expressed by physical movement: in the Clarinet Concerto the soloist moves among the orchestral players, goading them and even playing from their music. In the Horn Concerto the soloist controls and directs the orchestral horns, who move around the auditorium. Other composers in the 1960s and '70s were using spatial deployment (Birtwistle's *Verses for Ensembles* springs to mind), but Musgrave's approach is so individual and successful that the works must count among the major achievements in British music of the time. Since the concertos Musgrave has concentrated on a series of dramatic and lyrical operas and vocal works; it is a shame that works like *Mary, Queen of Scots* have not been heard in Scotland for many years.

Judith Weir, born in England in 1954, comes from an Aberdeen family and clearly feels a strong attachment to her Scottish roots. She knows the country, its people, its history and culture, and its folk music. As a teenager she played oboe and percussion in the National Youth Orchestra of Great Britain, learned the violin and took composition lessons with John Tavener. She studied at King's College, Cambridge – one of the first women allowed in! – with Robin Holloway, and has had a variety of employments since, including Southern Arts Association's Composer in Residence (1976–79), and Cramb Fellow at Glasgow University (1979–82). She began to compose full-time when she was awarded the Creative Arts Fellowship at Trinity College, Cambridge, (1983–85); and a series of major commissions has enabled her to continue without teaching commitments – including the BBC-commissioned opera *A Night at the Chinese Opera* (1987), and Glasgow District Council's 1990 'European City of Culture' commission for Scottish Opera, *The Vanishing Bridegroom.*

Weir, like most composers, strives for an individual voice, but to an unusual degree. She particularly admires composers who work outside the mainstream of western classical music, those who abandon the orthodoxies in search of something special and original, such as John Cage, John Tavener, Michael Finnissy and Sir Peter Maxwell Davies. She has drawn considerably on folk music material from Scotland, China, and Eastern Europe, and on mediaeval music. Much of her music is chamber music in the truest sense, and often written for specific players.

Weir has written in all genres. Her music can sound deceptively simple – a solo line with accompaniment – and is notated in conventional manner. The Scottish element is evident in *ceol beag*-influenced simple rhythmic structures, diatonic harmonies, but also in the *ceol mor*-influenced microtonal complexities and chromatic harmonies. Examples of this include *Scotch Minstrelsy* and the *Sketches from a Bagpiper's Album.* Her style is inherently dramatic: so many of the works have a programmatic element, a pre-text or underlying plot. She composed three short 'operas' – *King Harald's Saga* (for a soprano singing eight parts), *The Black Spider* and *The Consolations of Scholarship* (based on Yuan opera) – and *A Serbian Cabaret* before writing her first full-length opera, *A Night at the Chinese Opera.* This work established Weir as one of the foremost young British composers. In it she takes the declamatory recitative style of Chinese opera and uses it to her own ends to explore the means of conveying words by music – an exploration which began in *The Consolations of Scholarship* and continued in *The Vanishing Bridegroom*, and the television opera *Scipio's Dream* (a re-composition of Mozart's *Il Sogno di Scipio*).

Other aspects of Weir's music which particularly strike the listener are her humour, her use of minimal techniques, and her grasp of form. Her musical imagination and style, especially the way she seamlessly merges old and new techniques and philosophies, are very individual. Few composers have found such a unique voice so early in their careers. Since 1990 Weir has written a number of chamber works, two orchestral pieces, and an opera for English National Opera is due later this year.

Whereas Weir and Musgrave are established Scottish composers now living outside their homeland, Sally Beamish is an Englishwoman who has chosen to settle here, and whose composing career has only recently begun. Born in London in 1956, she began playing and writing music at an early age, later studying the viola and composition with Anthony Gilbert and Sir Lennox Berkeley at the Royal Northern College of Music. For a decade she made her career as a viola player, mainly in London, as Principal Viola of the London Mozart Players, a member of the Raphael Ensemble, and as a freelancer with among many ensembles and orchestra, the Academy of St Martin's-in-the-Fields, Lontano, and the London Sinfonietta. She was also for a while Principal Viola in the Scottish Chamber Orchestra. In 1989 Beamish received an Arts Council Composer's Bursary (and gave birth to her first child) and decided with her husband, the Scottish cellist Robert Irvine, to move to Scotland, where he is Principal Cello with the Orchestra of Scottish Opera. Since moving to Scotland Beamish has given up the viola to concentrate on composition, and during these past three years her career has begun to flourish – thanks initially, she says, to the patronage of her husband, who afforded her child care so that she could compose. She has received commissions for chamber works from among others the Hebrides and Raphael Ensembles, and the Cheltenham Festival. She has been one of the composers to take part in the Scottish Chamber Orchestra's pioneering education projects. Her first symphony was commissioned by the City of Reykjavik and premiered there in January 1993. Other 1993 premieres included an oboe concerto *Tam Lin* for the Premiere Ensemble, and a work for the Scottish Ensemble. Also in 1993 Beamish received a Paul Hamlyn Foundation Award for outstanding achievement in composition, which she plans to use to take composition lessons (memories of Helen Hopekirk!). Premieres in 1994 include a violin concerto commissioned by the BBC Scottish Symphony Orchestra, and a symphonic work for the Academy of St Martin's-in-the-Fields. And over the next few years she will be writing for the BBC Singers, London Philharmonic Orchestra, and the London Mozart Players. With Robert Irvine and composer James MacMillan she has formed the Chamber Group of Scotland, which specialises in performances of contemporary music, especially music not otherwise performed in Scotland.

Beamish's music uses the lingua franca of British composers of the late 20th century, but by virtue of her preference for lyricism, tonal centres, strong rhythms, the dramatic, and her sense of humour, she has found her own distinct and accessible voice. Her music, like Weir's, can sound deceptively simple. Her training and career as a top string player have enabled her to work with the finest musicians, conductors and composers, and given her a tremendous knowledge of the repertoire, and insight into the techniques of composition and the technical possibilities of both instruments and voices. Most of her works have a programmatic background, not always so evident in the finished product, and she has a preference for biblical and poetic texts. Her move to Scotland opened up for her the wealth of Scottish traditional music, which has influenced particularly her choice of musical form – a *piobaireachd* underpins both her string trio *Piobaireachd*, and the first symphony.

Beamish has constantly resisted the image of 'mother-of-two and composer' foisted upon her by the press. To her composition is a creative urge which must be fulfilled, and is no different from being a performing musician and a mother – worktime and family life still have to be juggled.

To summarise the current situation of women in music in the UK generally but specifically in Scotland, I would say that things have never looked so good. There are jobs, career opportunities, even, apparently, equal opportunities. But in common vocabulary a musician, a composer, is still perceived as a male figure. Though at school level music is seen predominantly as a "girl's subject", and equal numbers of young women and men are taking music at higher education level, women still represent a minority of professional performers, and performances of works by women composers are infrequent. The problem for women composers – as discussed above – is probably less one of acceptance of their work than a reflection of the fact that few women aspire to work in this area, partly due to a perceived lack of possibilities.

In music management women are holding a greater percentage of middle and lower management positions – in administration, marketing or personnel. This is because on the whole they are better at 'people-orientated' jobs – which tend to be fairly badly paid. Artistic direction and executive management remains firmly in the hands of men – there are few women at decision-making level. There are not enough women on boards, and even fewer chairwomen. And without women in these top positions to encourage other women, and to demonstrate to men their abilities, the glass ceiling will not be raised.

The quality and quantity of women's contribution to Scotland's musical life cannot be underestimated. I hope that this fairly brief and cursory overview will bear this out. But there is no room for complacency. I look forward to a time when we have women as chief executives of some of our national bodies – and more women on the podium. But that's another story...

Ann McKay

Athole Christina Cameron

born Glasgow, 13 January 1923
died Edinburgh, 6 May 1992

Teacher, writer, and nationalist, Athole Cameron divided her energies throughout her life.

The teacher came first. Brought up in the schoolhouse at Glenlyon, Perthshire, where her mother was the teacher, Athole trained at Dundee College of Education, taught in Perthshire schools, and latterly was head teacher at Howgate School in Midlothian.

She joined the Scottish National Party as a young woman, and stood for Parliament three times. How she would have relished taking on the Westminster Club if enough of the voters of Dunfermline or Inverness had given her the chance. She was a practised orator whose contributions to debates at the party's National Conference and reports as convener of the Heritage Society always entertained as well as enlightened the assembled delegates.

In retirement she was discovered by the media, shining as one of the first contestants in BBC Scotland's *SuperScot*, and becoming a vocal regular on the *Scottish Women* forum on STV.

Writing was wedged in when space and time allowed, or the challenge of a competition proved irresistible. She wrote plays, short stories and poems – the best of her work being in Scots. Her love of the theatre began early when, as an enthusiastic teenager, she spent many happy hours front-stage and behind the scenes at Perth Theatre. She went on to write several plays and to be a producer with Community Drama, and her play *The Eve of Saint Paul*, based on an incident in Perth in 1544, was given a public reading at the Traverse Theatre, Edinburgh.

In her poems we can find distilled all the loves of her life. Her abiding passion for her country – its people, its history, its beauty and its music – was the inspiration for much of her poetry, but she was concerned too with the future wellbeing of the world. And she did so love cats.

Would that she had found time to write more poems, but there is enough here to give a flavour of a most remarkable Scot.

Margaret Macaulay

Song for Roro in Glenlyon

This was a town: pause where the stones lie scattered.
A town where men were glad, a town where nobody mattered.

This was a town, and now is a field of sheep.
Go on your ways, the hills have a tale to keep.

A tale of laughter and life, and grazing sheep and cattle,
Of men who warred with beasts, and did not win the battle.

Memo to nice persons

We were not meant for agony
The intelligent classes
Raised up by a sound education
A little above the masses.
Not ours the passionate seeking
The scream in the dark
The lonely tempest of weeping
The bench in the park.
For we love open fires
And cushions and cups of tea
The frightened cries of the sordid
Are nothing to such as we.

We were not meant for disaster
No earthquake shakes us
We sigh while repairing the plaster
Abstaining from fuss.
Heartbroken we fall on jogging
Till counting the cost
We find but some tears and a token
And a few kisses lost.
For we can look forward with prudence
We are not afraid of the dark
We think about Art and the angels
We walk before noon in the park.

We were not meant for tragedy
The respectable classes
Instructed in fiction and history
We know that everything passes.
We do not approve of the drama
The suicide pact
We know that all things can be settled
By money and time and tact.
So we follow the signposted pathway
In quiet and conservative hats
And the passionate fires of the outcasts
Discreetly include in our chats.

Ponies at Cathlaw

Out of the eddying mist
a herd, a drift,
a menace of ponies,
the power and the dream
and the loss, incarnate.

On this cold hillside
older than Scotland
hooves of Pictish ponies
thunder and pass
in a whisper of history.

Soft as the mist
the gentle Celts
long gone, the dead
and the living meet
in the cold soil's homage.

Where the flower of a dream
unchoosing must bloom
in its season,
where a stream's first surge
sets for the sea.

Brooding, the herd
and the hillside wait,
as moving shadows loom
mist-drenched
on the paths of men.

Sixteen

I am myself. There is nothing that you can do.
I am myself, and that not one or two
but fifty selves, and each one in its turn
can laugh and love and cry, can hate and hope and yearn,
and have its hour, and pass, and there is nothing more.
I am myself. There is no key to my door.

And so it does not matter if we kiss
or that the moon is high on summer nights.
When dawn is come, an ending to all this
there will be other joys and soft delights
and other dreams and fears, until the times grow cold
and I am left alone in the dreaming days of the old.

Yet still myself. There is nothing that you can do.
When I am grown old I will not remember you.

Progress

He took his muckle bulldozer
an dung doon
the auld castle biggin
wi a its aipple trees
that sclimmed doon

tae the burn side
an wrocht a braw toom prairie
for growin his wheat.
"Man," he said,
"is man no clever?"
But there was naebody left
tae hear him.

He took his muckle tractor
an dung doon
the gowans an the celandines
an a the peesweeps' nests
an ilk wee leevin thing
that micht get in the road
o the technological revolution.
"Man," he said,
"is man no clever?"
But there was naethin left
tae hear him.

He took his muckle missile
an dung doon
the hale jing-bang
o their bit
o the warld.
Twa seconds syne
they did as muckle for him.
"Man...

For the Lang-deid Seceders

"In memory of a portioner in Howgate and his son, a minister of the Seceder kirk."
Gravestone, St Mungo's Kirkyard, Penicuik

Ice-shot frae the Siller Burn, the gale
Sooms ower the Moss
Dirlin the fanklet thorns wi progs o hail,
Skirlin fur loss.
The lowerin day drags ahint Scald Law,
The morn we'll see snaw.

Snod i the neuk o the brae
In Saint Mungo's ward
They bide happit deep an still
For their kent reward,
Crofters o Howgate, wrights
Frae the Siller Burn,
Hard darg wi sma return.

Heich on the frostit hill whaur the loanin rins
Oot owr tae the Ha's
The leme o the dyin day lichts owr the braes
Tae the hawthorn raws,
An the berried hert flares reid
In a blazin lowe
I the briest o the dour herd howe.

The rigs they wrocht are lang-syne smoored in gress,
Their dour faith tint.
Nae mindin too o the dree o the herd day's darg
For them that come ahint,
Or o them that siccar held, leal i the deid o the year,
The lowe that maun abide,
The hert o the ward-fire's leme on the stey brae-side.

Ginger Cat

Gowd, i the gowd
o flamin leaves,
a sleekit glory
o lurkin ill.

Ae fleetin sang,
nae mair.
A blaze o death,
pet-purrin.

Catriona NicGumaraid

Uilebhheist

O uilebheist, uilebheist tha suidh' air mo ghualain,
Uaireannan do-fhaicte, uaireannan gun fhaicinn
O uilebheist, uilebheist teich bhuam!
O uilebheist, uilebheist tha suidh' air mo ghualainn,
Uaireannan le dranndan, uaireannan a' sgreuchail
Le bhian a' seasamh le cathach,
Fhiaclan a' snapadh le cobhair
Uilebheist, uilebheist cum bhuam!

Monster

O monster, monster that sits on my shoulder
Sometimes impossible, sometimes invisible
O monster, monster, flee from me!
O monster, monster that sits on my shoulder,
Sometimes moaning, sometimes screaming
Its fur standing in rage,
Its teeth snapping with foam
Monster, monster keep away from me!

Women in the Tradition

Sheena Wellington

Some years ago, during a concert in Edinburgh, I happened to remark that I believed the very first singers were women, as the very first songs must have been lullabies. A charming and erudite man approached me later in the evening to tell me that I was wrong and that human singing began with the work song. I could not resist asking him if he had ever paced the floor at 2am with a teething, colicky, girning bairn – now that *is* hard work!

More recently, in the course of a series of lectures, I played versions of 'Durisdeer', 'Flowers o the Forest', and 'The Laird o Cockpen' to a class and asked them to find a common link. Despite the fact that this particular talk was subtitled 'Women and Song', no one made the obvious connection that the lyrics of all three were indeed written by women, Lady John Scott, Jane Elliot and Carolina Oliphant, the Lady Nairne, respectively. The curious invisibility of the creative and interpretative energies of women in all of the arts does extend, although to a lesser degree, to the public perception of traditional music.

Few scholars would dispute the vital role of women as tradition-bearers and song-carriers. The collections of Bishop Percy, David Herd, Robert Burns, Walter Scott, William Motherwell and Francis James Child were heavily dependent on material garnered from women, whether it was 'the singing of a country lass' (probably Jean Armour), the redoubtable Mrs Brown of Falkland or James Hogg's mother, and in recent times no one could doubt the importance of Lucy Stewart, Jessie Murray, Belle and Sheila Stewart, Lizzie Higgins and the incomparable Jeannie Robertson. The devotion of Percy and Scott to the notion of the wandering minstrel, with his courtly and polished phrases, as the main source and succour of the ancient balladry probably owes as much to a romantic turn of mind as to any historical record. There were minstrels, of course, talented musicians earning a living in the service of a chief or laird, or as medieval buskers travelling from settlement to settlement; and they undoubtedly composed songs and tunes, but they also garnered material from those they met on their travels, whether in hall or kitchen, in castle or rough cottage. And the minstrels were by no means always men. The 14th century Meg of Abernethy was a noted clarsach player, and there are records of payments to women singers. John Purser's excellent *Scotland's Music* records, from 1506, "Item, to tua women that sang to the king, eighteen shillings.", a sum large enough in the context of the time to suggest that these were professional singers.

However, traditional music, and particularly song, does not depend on a formal setting or a state occasion for its transmission. It belongs first and foremost to the home, to the family, to the neighbourhood. Even today, in spite of TV, CD and the dread Nintendo, many a household knows the glorious sound of the human voice raised in song. True, it may be 'Young at Heart' rather than 'Leesome Brand' but the principle holds. There are very few women, whether they think of themselves as singers or not, who have not sung to their small children, whether it be bairns' sangs, big ballads or pops – and haven't we all told stories? I have frequently found in a family of fine singers that Father is convinced that he is the inspiration, he is the one who sings at weddings and other semi-public occasions and his wife is 'nae singer ava', while his children will tell you that they learned most of their songs from their mother whose antidote to the monotony that is most forms of housework was to sing.

There is, of course, scant evidence of the authorship of most of the great ballads, and only surmise is possible – a feeling that the literally hellish fate prophesied for 'The Cruel Mother' speaks for the genuine religious (superstitious?) terror of a woman guilty of infanticide may say more for my imagination than for any proof there may be – but there can be no doubt that the generations of women who have sung them have played an important part in shaping the variations.

Within the ballad stories themselves, women play a major role, and by no means are they always the helpless victims. The third sister in 'Babylon', unaware at the time that the attacker is her brother, is brave and cool-headed; the heroine of 'The Knight and the Shepherd's Daughter' shows commendable persistence in tracking down her seducer, and one can only hope that she was happy with the resultant marriage; and the glorious 'Eppie Morrie' resists her abductor's assault on her virginity with effective determination, leaving her triumphant, and him totally and deservedly humiliated. Womankind is very well represented by the courage of Lady Margaret defying an overwhelming force in 'The Bonnie Hoose o Airlie', the fortitude and tenacity of the faithful wife successfully pleading for the life of 'Geordie' and the quick wit of the heroine who bests the devil in 'Riddles Wisely Expounded'.

Women have, too, some of the best and wisest lines. The mother in 'The Fair Flower o Northumberland', possibly with a fond recollection of a youthful escapade of her own, welcomes her disgraced daughter with the comforting:

> Ach you're no the furst that the Scots hae beguiled
> – An you're aye the Fair Flower o Northumberland!

Peggy Coutts, the shepherd's lassie, lowborn bride of 'The Laird o Drum' can "neither read or write, nor was she bred at the school" but on her wedding night she has the wit to counter her bridegroom's complaint about her lowly status with a clear and clever rendering of both nuptial and natural law:

> I telt ye weel afore we wed, ye wer faur abuin my degree, O
> But noo we are merried, in ae bed laid, ah'm jist as guid as ye, O
>
> An when ye are deid an I am deid, an baith in ae grave lain, O
> An seeven years doon an lifted again, they'd no ken your dust fae mine, O

Family disapproval of this match seems to have softened by the way – on the death of Irvine of Drum, the lady married another Irvine, Irvine of Cults.

Nor do women lack representation as villains of the piece. 'Bonnie Barbara Allan', like her male counterpart 'Lord Lovel', is probably guilty of no more than pride and insensitivity, but the nurse in 'Lamkin', the unseen poisoner in 'Lord Randall', the wife of 'The Baron o Brackly' and Lady Erskine in 'Child Owlet' are all depicted as thoroughly evil, capable of acts of savagery and betrayal which, retold by a singer of the calibre of Anne Neilson or Jo Miller, can chill the blood and haunt the memory.

The ancient, atavistic fear of women emerges in the balladry, too, not only with the witch 'Alison Gross' and the Fairie Queen in 'Tam Lyn' being credited with supernatural powers: a seemingly ordinary woman like the mother-in-law in 'Willie's Lady' can call on uncanny forces to prevent a child's birth, and it is the stepmother in 'Kemp Owyne' who casts the spell turning her lovely stepdaughter into the ugly and savage beast who can only be redeemed by a kiss from the hero. It is the ghost of a woman, a rejected lover, who wreaks grotesque revenge in 'Willie's Fatal Visit':

> An she has taen her perjured love, and reived him frae gair tae gair
> An on every style o Mary's kirk, o Wullie she's hung a share

The only other truly violent spirit in the ballad canon is 'James Harris, the Daemon Lover' but he is an incarnation of the devil rather than a revenant.

Violent death is central to many of the ballads and both men and women meet horrifying ends. Often, though, the fate of the women casts an interesting light on prevailing attitudes. 'The Cruel Brother' feels it is his right to stab his sister on her wedding day because the bridegroom has neglected to ask his consent to the match; in the incest ballad 'Sheath & Knife' Willie kills his sister and their child and returns heartbroken to his home to find that a party, presumably to celebrate the tidying up of the problem, is in full swing; and 'The Death of Queen Jane' does not prevent celebration of the birth of an heir to the throne.

In one of the most poignant of the ballads, known, strangely, to most women singers as 'Mill O Tifty's Annie' and to most men singers as 'Andrew Lammie', the young heroine compounds the error of falling in love with the wrong man, a trumpeter and reputed warlock, by dismissing the slightly ambiguous advances of the local landowner –

> Had she been born o a richer kin, as she is rich in beauty,
> I would hae taen the lass masel, and made her my ain lady.

With a proud and decisive –

> O Fyvie's lands are far and wide, and they are wondrous bonny
> But I widna gie my ain dear love, no for a yer lands o Fyvie!

During the subsequent beating by her brother, Bonnie Annie's back is broken – in some accounts "ower the Temple stane", in others "ower the high ha door" – a brutal punishment by any standard. History does not record what punishment, if any, was visited upon her killer.

We have already noted that some of Scotland's best-loved songs were written by women, usually of noble, or at least wealthy, position and of these none was more prolific, more influential or more reticent than Carolina Oliphant of Gask, later to be Lady Nairne. Ambitious, as have been so many before and since, to 'purify' the national song she was equally determined to ensure that her name should not be linked with her work, and her songs originally appeared under a variety of aliases, the best known being Mrs Bogan of Bogan.

This, of course, led to much speculation, even during her lifetime, and she had the experience of hearing 'The Land o the Leal' being attributed to Robert Burns, it being thought to have been written while he was on his deathbed, and originally addressed to 'Jean'. Like Burns, Lady Nairne set her lyrics to traditional melodies and this further confused the issue. Several Victorian songbooks credited songs like 'The Lass o Gowrie' and 'The Auld Hoose' to Burns, and I recently had a difference of opinion with a musician who insisted that Robert must have written 'The Rowan Tree', partly on the strength of an old book, but mainly, and quite outrageously, in the mistaken belief that Carolina was not capable of 'real' poetry. True, she could write as sentimentally and with as much romanticised patriotism as any other Scot of her day and class, but she also had the gift of putting into words the very deepest feelings, and finding the right melody to suit. 'Caller Herrin' with its searing lines

> Wha'll buy ma caller herrin,
> Oh, ye micht ca them vulgar farin,
> Wives an mithers maist despairin
> Ca them lives o men!

set to Nathaniel Gow's beautiful melody is heartbreaking.

The major contribution that women have made to Gaelic poetry and song is universally accepted. Best known among the bardesses of the Gaeltacht is probably the seventeenth century Mary MacLeod whose poetry is most wondrously singable. She was also, by most accounts, a bit of a tadger, and was at one time banished from the MacLeod household, but she has left a legacy of powerful song, including 'Hilliu-an, Hillio-an' and several delightful flyting pieces. Like many other talented women she was suspected of witchcraft and when she died at the remarkable age of ninety-one she was, by her own wish, buried face down. Whether this was an admission of guilt or a last act of defiance must remain a matter of conjecture. The other great Gaelic bardess of the late seventeenth and early eighteenth century was the harper Sileas MacDonald of Keppoch whose name is now very fittingly born by two of our most gifted and adventurous musicians, Patsy Seddon and Mary McMaster, who form the harp duo Sileas.

It is women, too, who created that most compelling of work-related chants the Oran Luadhaidh or Waulking Song. Used to relieve the monotony and sheer physical labour of waulking the tweed, these songs, often borrowed and altered rhythmically to fit, have a universal appeal. I recently took part in a workshop in Barcelona where a group of Catalans gave 'He Manda' laldy as they enthusiastically waulked a blanket borrowed from our hotel. Gaelic song without women is unthinkable!

Anyone with a knowledge of today's traditional music scene is aware of the key role that women have as tradition-bearers and, also, in the forefront of the continuing creative process that is the living tradition. To name but a few, and in no particular order, any list of fine ballad singers would include Elizabeth Stewart, Maureen Jelks, Heather Heywood, Margie Sinclair, Gordeanna McCulloch, Janice Clark, Gerda Stevenson and many more. The great Flora McNeill MBE did much to rescue the reputation of Gaelic song from the satin-lined straitjacket in which a combination of the formality of the Mod and the ineffable Kennedy-Fraser sugar-coating had placed it. Today, Christine Primrose, Eilidh MacKenzie, Cathie-Ann McPhee and the irresistible Iseabail NicAsgaill are carrying on the work. The clever, lyrical, funny and poignant songs of writers like Nancy Nicolson, Janet Russell, Sheila Douglas and Gill Bowman have passed into the standard repertoire.

Jeannie Robertson bearing the tradition, c1963

Instrumentally there has been an explosion of interest and participation. The clarsach has led the way here, thanks to the efforts of Comunn na Clarsach, with Alison Kinnaird, Isobel Mieras, Charlotte Petersen, Mary Ann Kennedy and others now passing on their skills as well as performing, and Savourna Stevenson writing the most challenging and exciting new harp music around. Fiddlers are very much to the fore with Carmen Higgins, Marie Fielding, Maureen Turnbull and Debbie Scott among the best. Deirdre Adamson and Lindsay Weir are just two of the excellent young accordion players that come to mind and Blo Na Gael's brilliant whistle player Helen Forbes has a sublime talent. A noticeable and pleasing feature of instrumental workshops these days is that the sexes tend to be fairly evenly balanced, and the average age is young – in some cases very!

Like women, the traditional arts of music, song and story are remarkably resilient. They can survive wars, famines, multiple emigrations, and social upheavals of every kind remaining, if not quite unscathed, at least recognisably themselves.

Oh, and I am still convinced that a soft rhythmic chant to soothe cavebaby was the beginning of song, and the beginning of the crucial role which women have always played in the traditional arts!

Sheena Wellington

Lydia Robb

Dundee Day Tripper

The ither day
a tramcar cam
rummlin doun
the Nethergate
o ma memory.

It stoaped ootside
the Greens Playhoose
whaur an auld film
flickert backarties
in black an white.

Ootbye a puckle
camsteerie cooncil chiels
got cairried awa wi themsels,
yoked up a Trojan cuddy
an ploud throu the Overgate.

Craws cowpit
fae the corbie stanes
an the auld toun
turnt tae stour
happit harns in hodden grey.

The bummer gaed.
Words skellt fae
the mou o the
Courier biggin,
fell on deif lugs.

At the terminus
ma lines got raivelt,
left ma thochts
hingin like the washin
on the plettie.

Wash day sonnet

Aam keekin throu a telescope the wrang
wey roun. The washin-hoose is wabbed wi steam;
ma mither in a peeny tied wi twine
has 'Sunlight' soap-suds stipplin her skin.
She fills an auld zinc bucket tae the lip
wi watter fae the well. She smells o bleach.
Ma faither's sarks are tethered tae the rope

wi wuiden pegs. The mangle haunle creaks.
A saft slurry o stairch anoints the linens.
Fae in alow the byler lid, the fent
miasma o moth-baas an steepin woollens.
Fragmentit images growe indistinct:
a windae hauds her sheddae in its frame,
her distant simmers spun wi daisy-chains.

The Diagnosis

for Ian

He's been tellt
he has nae future.
Ye switch aff;

listen tae the
soun o the engine,
tickin tae a stop.

Hark at the houlet
i the wuid,
wyvin a waefu sang,

a lang drawn oot O.
Nicht is turnin
on a sternie.

See the siller sickle
o a laid-back mune
lichtin the laund.

The end-rig is in sicht,
the quernstane atween
Winter an Spring.

We Kin Laffatit Noo

The lie brurry
thats whurrit wiz
a poetry re
ding by
whitziz name

red uz
a six wurd poem
wi the
obligiturry
four letter wurd
thrownin
turdsanat
ken

right enuff
tellt uz
his languij
wiz disgraceful

red uz anither
that soondit like
a shoapin list

we dun
the wrang thing
snickert

shooda seeniz face
he sez
tipicil
thickiz shitn
a boatl
the lottya

ah gee up
kenma
heed duzny
buttn
up the back
if ye dinny unnerston
jiss fuckaff
gawn
ootma road

Christine De Luca

Body Chemistry

Can I believe you are
no more than atoms reeling
in intimate bombardment?
(Even when you sleep, they dance.)
And that your molecules
bonded this way and that
just hold back chaos?
What random wobbling
to produce such subtlety!
What sub-atomic spaces!
What emptinesses
to create such stature!
Such galaxies of wonder
is a man!

Private Laand

Faces fornenst windows we stimed,
cuppit haands blockin oot da licht.
Ony a coose o bruck ta see. — *heap of refuse*

On a knowe ahint da Haa
a scorie croogit in a røfless to'er; — *crouched*
wis hit whar ladies sippit tae
or whar da laird wid set his gless
apo sixerns in truck ta him — *fishing boats*
ta ken whar dey wid laand
der catch?

De'er aa gien noo:
a wye a life turned headicraa
vod is der haa. — *empty as their house*

I da kirkyerd
fenced aff fae aabody
der's a rød o wirds — *empty prattle*
apon a muckle stane;
an nettles cled
der hidmost privacy. — *final*

Focal Length

From the train, the view today
is monochrome. Rain rivets
sea and sky and land:
shades of grey reflect
the inner eye. I hesitate
to check my colour vision
against clothes of passengers.

My eye is drawn
to drops of water
on the window: they race
like frantic sperm
across the glass.
Only raindrops,
yet they pull the focus short;
shut out landscapes
beyond reason.

A day ago,
through the same window,
there were a thousand
bright vanishing points.

Fowl Play

He's a handsome bird, the ostrich
with a lot to flaunt: fine feathers
and a now-protected tail.
His plumes have graced coquettes
and chorus lines; trimmed
hats and bodices:
sent frissons through audiences.

His legs, built with karate in mind
edge out his rivals; acceleration
is galvanic. His flightless wings
with white designer trim
seem to impress:
the mating dance, primeval, unrehearsed:

three times, three partners
a clutch of twenty eggs:
three simultaneous families reared as one.
He bides his time, then when he's done his bit
by his arithmetic
he's up and off, head high
fast as a car. The females cry

and put their heads together
in the sand, to cool off presumably
or plot to even up the score.
The young ones tend to learn no more
than sex, survival of the fit.
Sharp exits and stunning entrances:
that's the way it is, with ostriches.

Tagidderness

a reflection on marriage

Twa hill lambs	
fae uncan aerts,	*unfamiliar places*
– een black an halliget,	*one, wild*
een moorit, mair perskeet –	*brown, prim*
ta'en fae da heogan	*common hill land*
tae a park inbye;	
cringed an teddered:	*tied together*
morroless.	*not a matching pair*
Little winder	
sae clos yokit, een poos	*pulls*
fornenst da tidder.	*against the other*
Hit taks a while	
at best, ta muv as wan,	
at warst, ta thole; ta see	
dere's naethin waar as	
clossness, whin hit's	
reffelled up an wippit	*twisted*
in a snød	*tangle*

(First published in the *New Shetlander*)

Devotions

an acrostic prayer

Dear God. I haven't
Exactly come clean with you. I've been
Very secretive about my
Object of devotion: and those precious
Transgressions of the mind:
I'm afraid I've enjoyed them
Over and over. And I'm
Not very prayerful, and only
Slightly sorry.

Why Engender?

Leslie Hills

Engender is an organisation founded and funded by women for women to research women's lives and their histories and to use information and research networks to campaign to improve women's social, economic, personal and political lives. It is for all women who want to change the way power is distributed and wielded in Scotland. Engender works in a complementary way with other women's organisations.

In *Woven by Women* Margaret Bain, accounting for the lack of prominence of women in Scotland, wrote "...in a society which is essentially repressive and lacking in confidence, the weaker sections will be even more repressed and their achievements even more ignored." The intervening years have seen little change.

The British political establishment, of both the left and right, continued to act as though the interests of women could be effortlessly elided with those of men. Policies were set forth as preserving the rights of men, their wives and their families. As Esther Breitenbach wrote in the 1989 *Scottish Government Year Book*, "If we are to ask the question whether women in Scotland have made progress towards equality in the decade since Mrs Thatcher came to power, then the short answer is that they have not. The overall picture for women in Scotland is that in terms of work, income and housing their position relative to men's remains grossly unequal."

Issues of particular concern to women were not merely ignored: their existence was not recognised. Such specific policies as tax measures may have helped a few, but only a small number of the relatively advantaged.

Under John Major's premiership women in Scotland have fared no better. His much-trumpeted Opportunity 2000 initiative, energetically prosecuted by Lady Howe, is aimed at helping a small group of women crack the 'glass ceiling'. Women's representation in top jobs in industry and the professions and in public life remains derisory. The initiative ignores those women struggling at and below the poverty line. For them life has become far tougher. Women still suffer the effects of occupational demarcation; in a time when the state and society are withdrawing rapidly from any concept of communal responsibility for the care of the elderly, the young and the disabled, women's burdens as carers have grown enormously. While funding for women's refuges is threatened, violence by men against women and their children increases.

Women form the biggest percentage of the poor, the old and the low-paid – groups particularly hard hit by recession and cuts in social services and forming the weaker sections of society to which Margaret Bain refers. With deregulation in the labour market, low-paid and part-time workers, the majority of whom are women, have lost the protection of employment legislation and in particular of Wages Councils. Two thirds of workers protected by Wages Councils, destined for abolition, are women.

The destruction of what little provision there was for adequate childcare has meant that many women who want to work are unable so to do and are caught in the poverty trap. Scotland has the lowest provision of childcare in the EC. Low wages will not cover the costs of private child care. Many fall back on benefit and are again at the mercy of the punitive social security system.

Concentrating power in the South East has particularly negative effects on women, who tend to exercise their politics at local levels. Privatisation and centralising "rationalisation" further weaken women's control over their own lives. There are few women on the newly appointed Boards and fewer still are feminists.

There are many women journalists now working for Scottish newspapers, and many make an attempt to mirror and analyse the lives of women in Scotland. But they are vastly outnumbered by their male colleagues and only a few, notably Sue Innes in *Scotland on Sunday*, are able to state the feminist case, consistently, week in, week out. Maria Fyfe, MP for Maryhill, says "I find all the time that the political reporters are typically not the slightest bit interested in issues like childcare. They are only interested in women's issues when they are to do with sex – so it is an uphill struggle to get women's issues taken seriously." This quote appeared in *The Herald* on International Women's day 1993 on the Women's page. On the general news pages there are a few column inches which do not mention the astonishing variety of meetings, conferences, seminars and workshops held by women across Scotland to mark the day. Instead there is a large colour photograph. The picture, all cute and pink and ruffles, is of a fashion show. *The Scotsman* printed a picture of that same fashion show, captioned – Three Little Maids – as its only nod towards International Women's Day.

One of the few glimmers of light in the media is the success of *Harpies & Quines*, published by a collective in Glasgow. This splendid, controversial, feminist magazine gives a platform to women who have something to say which cannot be said elsewhere. It is irreverent, informative, entertaining, welcome, and answers a deeply-felt need.

Eleven years ago Margaret Bain wrote that if any child were asked to name famous national women the reply was unlikely to extend much beyond Mary Queen of Scots and Flora McDonald, and ascribed this to a fault in the system which has failed to compile and evaluate the significant deeds of Scottish womanhood. 1992 saw the publication of *Chambers Scottish Biographical Dictionary*. The index of contributors lists sixty-nine men and seventeen women. And it is interesting to note the great imbalance between the institutional status of the male contributors and the description of the majority of the women as freelance. Needless to say, the overwhelming majority of the biographical subjects are men. Subjects are chosen from fields of endeavour such as arts, sport and the military. Interestingly there is no literature field which might have gone some tiny way to redressing the balance. There are many glaring omissions. How, for example, can the omission of Judith Hart, long-serving MP and Cabinet Minister, be justified?

In 1992 Chambers also published an *Anatomy of Scotland.* There were eleven contributors, ten men and one woman. The Foreword states that this book "...is about how Scotland works. It is about who runs it, where power lies, and the way in which power is exercised." And indeed it is. In its detailed description of patriarchy, in terms of its stated intention, it cannot be faulted.

In the introduction Peter Jones discusses "the set of myths and assumptions about the nature of Scottishness that have over the years...coalesced to form the character of the nation as it sees itself today." He is using the definition of myth set out by Gray, McPherson and Raffe in *Reconstructions of Secondary Education; Theory, Myth and Practice since the War.*

> We do not mean by myth things that are thought to be true, but that are in fact always false; nor do we mean things that are valuable but are, in fact, beyond human attainment or consent. Instead we use the term myth to refer to a story that people tell about themselves, and tell for two purposes. These purposes are, first to explain the world, and second to celebrate identity and to express values.

The problem for women in Scotland is that these dominant myths which have "coalesced to form the character of the nation as it sees itself today", are at best gender-blind and at worst totally exclusive of women in Scotland. The history of women, their struggles and triumphs has not been absorbed by the dominant Scottish myth.

If women, realising the deeply negative effect that straining to accommodate themselves to the dominant myth has on them, their choices and their capacity for autonomous action, reject the myth, they are left in a very exposed position. Women also need to "celebrate identity and express value" to construct a myth which will incorporate women's stories and women's histories.

Attempts to celebrate identity in Scotland fall foul of a deeply misogynist society – a society demonstrating its misogyny in its press, its public life, its politics and the daily lives of women. The incidence of sexual assault even of very young girls, is very high, as Richard Kinsey has recently shown. (Survey of Young People, University of Edinburgh, 1991/2) Most women learn very young to keep their heads down, to placate, to ignore sexist "jokes" and degrading songs and to avoid trouble as far as is possible. In a brilliant evocation of an experience every woman in Scotland will recognise, Janice Galloway writes

> But I still hear something like him; the clink and drag from the close-mouth in the dark, coming across open and derelict spaces at night, blustering at bus stops where I have to wait alone. With every other woman, though we're still slow to admit it, I hear it, still trying to lay down the rules. It's more insistent now because we're less ready to comply, look away and know our place. And I still see men smiling and ignoring it because they don't give a damn. They don't need to. It's not their battle. But it was ours and still is. I hear my mother too and the warning is never far away. But I never could take a telling. ('Fearless', in *Blood*, Secker & Warburg, 1991)

In 1993, the seventy-fifth anniversary of the winning of the vote, women in Scotland are largely invisible. An archaic and corrupt political system affords the electorate little or no say in the way it is governed. Women are doubly disadvantaged by their gender and by the system of government.

After the April '92 election women recognised wryly the protests of their male friends that they had no autonomy and were at the mercy of a small group of men for whom they had not voted and who did not have their best interests at heart. For many women the election merely confirmed a growing alienation from the existing political parties and structures. The political parties in Scotland do not have a good record in their treatment of women and gender issues. Only twenty-two women have been elected to parliament since 1918 when women were first eligible. For many, especially for women on the left, the realisation that any change in the culture of Scottish politics was at best cosmetic, was bitter, disorientating and sad. It was also, however, energising. Energies which in the past had been channelled into electing men into a Parliament hampered by grotesque procedures and fruitless combative rituals were now set free.

Before the April 1992 election, the 'Changing the Face of Scottish Politics' conference held in Glasgow had more than two hundred participants, three of them men – and one of these, an MP, stayed only one hour, having remarked that one had to attend these things as the party needed to attract more women voters. The conference was about empowering women by getting more women into Parliament and about the implications of more women MPs for the lives of Scottish women. After April, the conference organising committee held a recall conference in Edinburgh. It was a lively and, under the circumstances, relatively optimistic affair and led to the setting up of a group to coordinate efforts to advance women's representation and access to political and public life.

It was in this context that the organisation and purpose of Engender was hammered out. The women who set out to form Engender looked at the patchwork that is the women's movement in Scotland and saw that what was missing was a mechanism for researching women's lives and gathering and disseminating information. If this sounds a dry affair, it should be said that Engender was born in passion, in anger and frustration. And there was much sport in its making.

It is an organisation formed and funded by women for women in order to collect and use information about and for women; to research women's lives and their histories; to use information and research networks to campaign to improve the lives of women in Scotland; to work with other women's organisations and to make a distinctive contribution which will complement their efforts.

The provision of information is crucial for the work of promoting greater visibility and representation and of changing the very nature of the moribund power structures and relationships which blight the lives of women in Scotland. We need information to make our case, to focus our work and to make ourselves heard. We need to recover and consider our history to celebrate our identity and express values.

Over the past year a small group of women have formulated Engender as a company and have taken the first steps in putting in place the structures needed, keeping in touch with members by newsletter and local meetings and by liaising with other women's organisations and participating in conferences and the Women's Coordination Group. There are working groups on finance and funding, membership, publicity, research, communications, planning, and information technology. Local groups have been formed to pursue local issues.

In February 1993 Engender was launched as a membership organisation. Membership is made up of a diversity of women, geographically, socially and politically. There have been many comments on the lines that not only was it high time but that the time was ripe. Members are participating in four ways. Some want to help fund activities which they value but are at present unable to pursue; others are working in local groups; others are contributing to and benefiting from the research and information function and others help in the running of the organisation. That is how it looks at the moment, but it will and must evolve, responding to the needs and at the behest of its members.

The first major project has been in response to the Women's Coordination Group's recognition of a need for much more and better information. The task of monitoring the progress, or lack of it, of women has been hampered by the absence of relevant data. Information is neither readily available nor accessible. That which is available is often difficult to locate, based on UK figures which are not broken down by country, region or gender, and often hopelessly out of date. As one of Engender's main aims was to establish an information network, we took on the task of collating information which is presently available and of producing a Gender Audit which surveys the position of women in a broad range of areas of public and political life. The Gender Audit has been extremely popular – the first print run has sold out and it is now being reprinted.

However, the function of the Gender Audit is to go beyond issues of representation and equality and to examine the position of women in relation to such issues as housing, health, domestic violence, the arts and poverty. It is only the beginning of a long-term project in which information will be gathered over time and monitored.

This work draws on information already available. One of the ongoing tasks of Engender will be to improve access to existing research on the lives of women and on gender issues. There is a considerable body of research scattered in libraries and filing cabinets across the country and needing to be liberated and used. Another ongoing task will be the creation and maintenance of a database of women with expertise and, crucially, experience that will be of help to others.

The experience of women in Scotland, very different from that of men, has been a well-kept secret. This experience must be described and analysed until through time it becomes part of the dominant myth and ensures that our children do not have to re-form the women's movement year after wearisome year.

In becoming part of the dominant myth it must change it. Engender is quintessentially about change. Women in Scotland are deeply dissatisfied with the society that men have made and the culture they have formed. It neither acknowledges women nor answers their needs and often is inimical to them. It causes a great deal of pain.

We are beginning to write our story. Every year a few more books are published, a few more plays performed and a few more songs sung. But the women who research and write and play and sing do so against tremendous odds, underfunded, underpaid, laden with responsibilities for dependents and at work, and against entrenched interests and extraordinary complacency. And who heeds their words? Sometimes it seems we are talking to ourselves. But we also need to talk to men and not only to the many men who support us and who also wish for change. There are many who see no need for change. Last year the Scottish Law Society opined that the moves towards equal opportunities being made by their fellows in England were not wanted here and that guidance or rules on discrimination for the legal profession in Scotland are not necessary. A working party report urging positive action on equal opportunities by the Scottish Law Society has been gathering dust for more than a year. Meanwhile the Glasgow-based Association of Women Solicitors has formed a sex discrimination committee and a working party. They are in for a tough time. But then as women in Scotland they must be used to that. May they flourish.

Leslie Hills for the Engender Interim Board

Underground

Marion Arnott

She hated the moment when the river of people flowed off the platform into the subway train and froze into a tight locked mass of jutting elbows, knees, brollies and brass-cornered briefcases. The sardine togetherness always made her claustrophobic, but today was much worse than usual. She was trapped in the centre of the aisle, wedged upright by the press of bodies all around her, with one arm pinned across her chest and the other bent at an uncomfortable angle behind her back. To make it truly unbearable, today was a rainy day and the smell of wet clothing and hair was overpowering. She swallowed hard and tried to relax, but she felt as though a snake were slowly twining round her rib-cage, and squeezing tighter and tighter; soon she would find it difficult to breathe, and the snake would wind all the way up to her throat and squeeze again until sweat broke out on her brow and black stars danced before her eyes. The fear of fainting and not being able to fall down made her heart hammer in her chest.

However, she knew a trick or two for dealing with claustrophobia. It was all a matter of self-control, and over the years she had mastered the art of forcing her imagination to take her away from the site of the crisis. She thought hard, and summoned up the image of high hilltops patched with snow and went for a climb up the slopes. She concentrated until she could feel springy turf underfoot and a keen wind slapping at her cheeks. As the image filled her mind, her breathing evened out and the snake fell away to the floor. If she made a really determined effort, she could make the climb last all the way to Hillhead station.

But her imagination failed her. Today the assault on her senses committed by the closeness of so many other people was particularly violent. She was inclined to blame the man standing directly in front of her. Her face was pressed into his chest and the deep slow rhythm of his heart was pounding in her ear; her cheek grew damp as his sweat seeped into the pores of her skin. He was breathing his expense account lunch right into her face, and what a charmless concoction it had been! There had been too much garlic, too many spices, and it had all been washed down by a particularly vicious red wine. It was the smell of the middle-class, middle-management executive, a familiar one on the Buchanan Street–Hillhead stretch of the line. His suit was damp from the rain and the pungent smell of wet wool caught at the back of her throat and choked her. She felt invaded as traces of him settled on her hair and clothes. It was strange that even though she could feel the weight of other people's bodies, contact with this man had a quality of deliberateness about it, was even vaguely threatening. Desperately, she tried to banish his solid bulk and heavy smells from her consciousness, but his presence was too strong for her. Panic seized her, and she fought for control.

She knew another mind-game. She focused on herself, trying to send her own presence out to battle with his. Her scent was a piercing floral one, more than a match for his aftershave; but his lunch had victory over her salad and orange juice; her PVC raincoat was no match for his stinking wool, but it was spattered with raindrops, and something of their sharp cleanliness penetrated the fog of panic in her head. She conjured up a soft and gentle mist of rain to drift around her, the kind of rain you get in Ireland where the air is cool and full of the tang of the sea. Gradually the man receded from her consciousness, blotted out by image after image of towering cliffs and rolling seas. She sucked in a lungful of air and began to relax, telling herself that it wasn't the man's fault the train was overcrowded; nor was it his fault that she was oversensitive to crowds; it wasn't even his fault that they were standing thigh to thigh with his hip-bone grinding into hers. She was very firm with herself: this was all accidental, unintended, and it really was time she got a grip on herself. The man faded into his true perspective and she dismissed him from her mind. Generously, she even forgave him his lunch before she mind-hopped back to Ireland.

She didn't stay there long. Not even the sight of the sun going down over Galway Bay would have been enough to cancel out the sensation of her wet mac riding up her leg. For a moment she was mystified, and then she turned cold from the bone marrow out as she registered the movement of a hand slithering up her thigh. With a furious jerk she swung her hips sideways to dislodge it, but it clutched at her leg, seized a chunk of flesh, and pinched hard. She bit back a yelp of pain and kicked at his shins, but there wasn't enough space to get any force behind it and her foot slid harmlessly across his ankle. Like a gentleman, he returned the gesture; thighs might be his thing, but he was willing to accommodate her tastes.

Her thoughts were scattering like sparks from a bonfire, and she could not think what to do next. A scream might help, but her throat felt as if it were stuffed with cotton wool and no sound would come out. If only she could free her arms, she might be able to reach down and push his hand away. She began to struggle. He seemed to like that a lot, because she heard the tempo of his heart go into double time, and the hand, scorching hot on her skin, became very agitated as he pushed harder against her. In a minute she would bite him. If only she could be sure he wouldn't take that as a sign of growing affection...

The hand was rapidly approaching lacy edges and the last resort. She was ready to bite, when suddenly it was all over. The train lurched, the crowd swayed, and one arm fell loose. In a flash, her hand shot down, seized his, and hauled it high in the air above her head, like a referee proclaiming the World Champion.

"Who's a naughty boy, then?" she yelled without thinking. She was appalled by the loudness of her own voice in the deep silence which fell over the compartment. Her heart quailed at the sudden publicity: she who lives by the sudden impulse will surely die of shame. Her only consolation was that he was equally exposed. He was frantically trying to edge away from her, but the crowd had closed in around them again, and he was held firmly in place. She dug her sharp nails into the palm of his hand and wondered how he liked the feel of *that*. She certainly enjoyed it. But now that she had him, what was she going to do with him? Would they have to stand in this grotesque minuet all the way to Hillhead?

She caught the eye of an enormous fat woman seated opposite. The woman was obviously enjoying the scene in front of her: her cushiony shoulders shook and her pillowy bosom heaved as she eyed the man up and down. Without warning, she filled the compartment with a deep coarse laughter, rich with contempt. "Ah've always wondered whit wan o *those* looked like!" she called out.

There was an answering ripple of light female laughter from all corners of the compartment, and dozens of pairs of eyes fixed on the man to inspect him. Their laughter fluted or trilled or flew sharp-edged like broken glass, but all of it beat round the head of the captive. She felt him sag slightly, doubtless trying to sink through the floor. She was more than avenged for her bruised pound of flesh, and she warmed to the solidarity she sensed in the other women. They had all experienced one of *those* in some form or another: gropers, phone pests and kerb-crawlers were an everyday hazard. But it wasn't every day that one of them was captured and put on display. Emboldened by a surge of pride, she decided it was time she knew what one of the faceless *those* looked like.

She gazed up at the steeple of their joined hands and saw a dark blue sleeve and a couple of inches of sparkling white cuff half-concealing a flat gold Rolex. Trash with class? She let her gaze wander over to his face. It was disappointingly normal: round, heavy-featured, a touch petulant because of the tension around his mouth. It was not a pleasant face, but there was certainly nothing to indicate his *Those*ness. She peered into his eyes. They were the colour of whisky and glowed with a sullen anger. This was a new experience for her; she had never before looked into the eyes of someone who seriously wished her dead. She grinned cheekily at him. She was safe enough. Deprived of the anonymity of crowds and shadows, and unable to depend on the silence of his target, his kind could never be anything more than ridiculous. He looked away.

She had an almost irresistible urge to ask him why he'd picked on her. Why had he thought she belonged to the gropeable class? After all they'd been through together, she felt she had the right to ask, but before she could speak, the train ground to a bone-jarring halt. Doors hissed open and there was room to move. The man wrenched his arm down and leapt a couple of feet away from her.

"Cunt!"

Which, she supposed, was all the explanation anybody ever got.

Marion Arnott

Men & Women & Writers' Groups

Valerie Thornton

"We're a bit short of women writers and I wondered if you had a story..."

At least he – it could never have been a she – was disarmingly honest, but yes, gender is an issue in writing, in publishing, and, more particularly, in writers' workshops.

As a tutor, no, as a female tutor to many writers' workshops over the last six years or so, roving to Lanarkshire, Ayrshire, Dumbartonshire and on home ground in Glasgow, I've observed the subtle impact of gender on the dynamics of writers' workshops.

There are three all-women groups that I've been involved with and about a dozen mixed groups.

If we pause first to think about the difference between men-only and women-only exclusivism, then we realise that the power balance is very different. When men get together and exclude women, it is done from a position of strength. They want to be boys together, whether it's the football team or the golf club, and women don't fit. Women are fine for making the tea or clearing up, but to be accepted on an equal footing is unthinkable. Admittedly, I'm citing an extreme position. Increasingly men are becoming aware of the imbalance in our society: some are even trying to do something about it.

However, when women-only groups are formed, they arise from a position of weakness, not strength. men are excluded because women are afraid of them. Men are good at dominating because they are bigger, stronger, louder and socialised to do so. Women are often afraid to be themselves in the company of men; in the company of those we have been socialised to defer to.

It's not good. It's not good for either men or women, and the sooner the relationship between the sexes becomes one of mutual respect, the better. Until then, I'll continue to find women-only groups among my workshops.

The first was short-lived. We met in a women's refuge in a small town with a high rate of unemployment. Learning how to express themselves in writing was the least of the problems for the few who could manage to get to our meetings. Beaten, abused and buckling under the burden of single-parenting, these women had to do all their writing within the meeting time because their lives were so fraught that they had no time to themselves.

No men were allowed into the building because they represented such terrors, and when a uniformed policeman – or, if you prefer, the local bobby – came in one December day to discuss his role as Santa Claus to the refuge crèche, one of the women in the writers' group exploded at him in a ball of screeching, kicking, clawing fury. We all had to restrain her and they told me later that she had a history of mental illness and could be very unpredictable.

The writings which came from them were achievements, although trying to convince them of that was very difficult. The workshop didn't last very long because of the enormous pressures on the women. It was also eccentric from the start because a writers' workshop was being offered more as diversion, entertainment and therapy, than in response to a request from a group of already-writers seeking guidance.

A second women's group met within the charming walls of a primary two classroom. We all perched on tiny chairs around tiny tables while the cherry trees flowered at all our windows. It lasted for only a few weeks. Again, they were troubled women who were reluctant to write, and fearful of reading out what they had written to three other sympathetic souls, and yet they were coming up with powerful memories and observations with which we could identify and empathise. Lack of numbers put paid to the funding for that group too and the blossom fell from all the trees.

And then there's my lovely group in Petersburn Library in Airdrie. An open day for women in autumn of '92 led to the formation of a writers' workshop, and we have been meeting fortnightly since then, with enormous success. In a women-only environment there is a pervading air of support and sympathy and friendliness. There is an ethos of equality and some women who might feel inhibited in mixed company are at ease expressing themselves. I guess it must be similar for men, although I suspect that male competitiveness gets in the way of sincere communication. That it does, if it does, is men's loss. Some of the beautiful writing about love and concern for their children, which has come from the women in Airdrie, would have the power to move men too, but there's the catch 22 – if there were men in the group, such writing might not have been deemed worth sharing, might well not have been written in the first place. We're all victims.

I believe that men are much more inhibited than women, when it comes to making themselves vulnerable, and that this prevents them from experiencing life at its fullest. In a writers' group you have to be vulnerable if you are going to gain anything from it. You have to dare to read your work aloud – and almost everyone prefaces their readings with an apology, self-deprecation, a denouncement of their work as slight and inadequate. They then have to submit to reactions, to critical appraisal, to praise, to encouragement. And that, I believe, is much more difficult for men than for women.

I've had several hundred people pass through the workshops I've taken and occasionally I encounter someone who professes to be a great writer. They are always men. One man arrived late, well after the tea-break – we always have a tea-break, with biscuits if we're lucky – on a bicycle. He disrupted proceedings extravagantly as he collapsed his bike in the school library where we were meeting, dug out some battered folders and fully expected us to stop everything and listen to his wonderful writing. He was a published writer – I think it was a letter to the local paper – and he was not very pleased when I thanked him for coming along, welcomed him to join the group and pointed out that as we had a lot of writing still to hear, perhaps he would like to bring his work back the following week when he could have some feedback. He didn't return. Maybe he had the wrong idea about writers' groups, but that overt arrogance (undoubtedly concealing a deep insecurity) would not have been displayed by a woman, and probably not to a male tutor.

Then there was another man, in another group, who had written four novels. None had been published. The fourth was about how the first three had been written. He read us an extract from his current novel, which needed a lot of rethinking, never mind re-writing, before it could approach being publishable. I asked him how he felt about it. "Great! Smashing! I love it!"

This is a key question. If anyone believes that their writing is perfect, I cannot help them. A writers' group cannot help them. And they *need* help.

The novelist came for three weeks. The second week he was late and had been drinking. The third week, he was very late, exuberantly drunk and devastated. "They've told me to fuck off!" he raged. He had received one of those reject letters, couched in the mildest of terms: "Thank you for letting us see your work... not quite appropriate for our list... wish you luck placing it elsewhere..." He wasn't daft. A rejection's a rejection and he didn't allow the phrasing of it to blind him to the reality. But behind that was fear. He couldn't face the possibility that perhaps his writing wasn't quite as good as he needed to believe it was. Unemployed, his self-esteem depended on him being a writer, and he knew in his heart that having written four novels wasn't good enough. I lost him after that day. I feel I have failed him, in that I hadn't managed to make him feel safe enough to dare to be vulnerable to help. I could have helped him, but he couldn't have let me.

It's the ones I lose that make me feel sad. But they often come with bigger problems than I could solve. However, in some ways the gender thing makes bigger victims of men than of women: the behaviours above are not part of women's ways of behaving, because the value-systems that lie behind them are different from those for women. Men tend to be reared in a competitive, aggressive and emotionally-repressed world; women tend to be reared more to care, be weak and emotionally expressive. I have had two women in different writers' groups who tried to dominate the groups verbally. They desperately needed to talk about the suffering and injustices they'd undergone and would preface the briefest of pieces with endless introductions, then tag on lengthy epilogues continuing their sorrows. It's a difficult line to draw, but the balance in a writers' group must be emphasis on the writing, rather than group therapy.

One of the most troubled men crossed my path recently. His mother had died of Alzheimer's disease three years before and he had nursed her and suffered the heartbreaking pain of public rejection by and abuse from his dying mother. He brought a twenty-page account of his suffering and wanted to read it to the group. He apologised in advance and said he might cry. He then read and cried and read and cried until I interrupted him and, as gently as I could, thanked him for letting us hear his writing. His effect on the group was disturbing: this overt display of misery troubled us all. He came back the next week, late and a little drunk. This time he read an article he'd written about Alzheimer's and again broke down. The following week he was later, drunker and wild. I said that it was probably better if he read something other than to do with Alzheimer's as it was distressing for us all to see him so upset. He didn't come back but he did send a note thanking us for our support.

Not that there isn't a place for emotion. People bring writing which makes us laugh, and sometimes a piece of writing will move us to tears. I've had dancing and singing in some workshops and the atmosphere when Jim, a wheelchair-bound stroke victim, sang 'September Song' in a thin but sure voice, is unforgettable. A strong and well-established group can expand to accommodate the extraordinary. And in such a group, both men and women can dare to be vulnerable. This is the way it should be. And at the end of such workshops there is a feeling of communion, of spiritual uplift. We know very little about each other's lives outwith the group, but the fun and social intimacy draw people back week after week and we all suffer withdrawal symptoms over the long enforced holidays.

As a female tutor, I've had one or two interesting encounters with men who feel threatened by a woman running the group; moreover a woman with a better track record as a writer than them. Doubly humiliating to the millstone male ego. They call me 'pet' and 'dear' and have an unshakeable faith in the excellence of their writing. Don't misunderstand, most men and most women are wonderful, but there are some situations where I'm in direct conflict.

I don't like working in an environment where people are smoking. Usually the premises are non-smoking anyway, but this is seldom observed. After a particularly bad week when my lungs ended up cluttered with smoke and my clothes were stinking, I put my foot down and said I didn't want anyone smoking. The passive majority of non-smokers were delighted; the smokers grumbled, challenged my right to ban it and capitulated, apart from Albert. Well aware of the smoking ban, Albert turned up late the following week with a pipe which he placed ostentatiously on the table. He sat next to me, sat back from the table and put his hands on his head attempting to assert his dominance over me and the group. I should have stopped him, but he lit his pipe and took a few puffs. Then, as pipes do, it went out. He did this a few more times and looks were exchanged in the group. The next time he made a move to do so, in the middle of someone reading, I whispered "Please don't smoke." He didn't.

At the end of the night, as several lit up cigarettes before leaving the room, a new member came up to me and asked what the policy was on smoking. Unaware that Albert was sitting behind me, I said "I ask people not to smoke here while the class is on and, fortunately, everyone is decent enough to go along with that." At this there was a strangled squawk from Albert. I thought I might have lost him then, however he turned up the next time without even a shred of shag. He still sits with his hands on his head but mutual tolerance and respect have been achieved.

It's very difficult to make valid assumptions about the effect of gender in writers' groups and what I have written here has been very subjective. The great majority of people who come to workshops are lovely, well-balanced and open-natured souls. The writing and discussion is always of interest and value. The biscuits range from nice to utterly delicious.

Women as victims, with their refuges and support groups, have a far higher profile than men, but I think it would be unfair to conclude that women are more victims than men. Women-only groups – women-only anythings – make the participants feel very safe and there is no doubt that some of the women who come to such groups would not come were they mixed. Ideally, mixed groups should also engender a feeling of safety – indeed the best do. What is missing, is perhaps men-only groups. The phrase 'men-only' comes tainted with pornographic associations, but I believe that if similar supportive and safe groups were offered to men, and if men could bring themselves to be vulnerable in a safe environment, then we would all benefit from enhanced self-knowledge and self-esteem.

Valerie Thornton

Once. Forever.

Valerie Thornton

I suppose breaking up must be romantic too, for the one who believes it will never happen. I wouldn't know. But I do know he won't let go. A lifetime of years of breaking up and now he holds on tighter than ever. Not to me. But around me, like bindweed curling its pretty choking bells around my feet and ankles, and on up to the throat.

Perhaps if he'd danced with me it would have been different. I wanted seduced in the sultry dark of the dance-floor. I wanted the weaving of desiring bodies, the mesmeric overtness of the display, the pride, the exhibition; the barely restrained greed, postponed into the dark blue hours of silver skins on pale sheets. But no. He doesn't like.

So we don't, have never, danced together.

I can feel others. The dark golden boy with the slant eyes and lips so seductive I could have watched him speaking forever. He spoke like a Frenchman, unconsciously kissing the words into life. And I drank them in. He danced with me. Once. Forever. In the long hot dark, we hesitated, lingering and shifting in the rhythm, a slow dark beat enveloping us, and drawing me into his darkness. His gesture was simple. He opened his arms to me. Once. Forever. And I melted to him. Him and me. We. Arms around, heads together mingling my dark hair with his darker hair, my perfume which was his perfume, his gin-and-bitter-lemon aftershave, intoxicating and cool, in the dark heat of the dance. I knew he could feel me, aching for him, against him; I could feel his dark desire in the secret warmth between us. Once. Forever. Until the song ended.

But this one has never danced. A lifetime of years of never dancing.

We should have been like cats, curled asleep together, nose to neck, breast to arm, hand to head, but no. Not he. He leaves me every night. Before, it was after. After the dark coupling, the brief proximity that lasted until after, when he turns and leaves. Leaves his back to me and heaves into sleep.

I knew one whose nose nestled in my neck long after. Long after we slept and dreamed, together and separately. One night in our sleep, his beautiful nose, which curved like Marlon Brando's and slept tucked against my throat, his arm enfolding me, he spoke of his love. But he named her Anna and shifted sweetly against me. Anna was not his name for me. Anna is my middle name, my mother's name, his wife's name. I kissed his temple and he woke a little, but not enough to know me.

There is a woman below my window. Four floors. Directly. I would land on her if I jumped. There is a pair of blue furry slippers at the foot of the orange rug on which she is sitting, her skirt pulled up to sun her legs. She has white hair, red nails and a wedding ring. She caresses a big black cat and moves her bag from one side to the other to make space for the cat. But the cat steps over her legs and sprawls on the grass, white paws to the sun, within reach of the red-tipped hand, lying still on the edge of the blanket. I wouldn't want to hurt the cat.

My cats creep in to me in the morning. They know the places against my shoulder, in the crook of my elbow, along my side where they can settle, purring, until we have breakfast, them and me. They know not to venture to the far side of the bed, beyond the back. If they go pawing and purring up to his face, they know his hand, like a paddle, will sweep them away from his precious dreams. I daydream and purr silently with them, in soft warm contentment.

Halfway through the years, he left. For months and months. Not for another, but for his love, the barren peaks and wastelands, high isolation, his only partner. We saw it coming. He said we would go away together, to real beds in guest houses, to the soft green hills nearby, to the wilds, to be alone, together. I dreamed of the bittersweet happiness of it, of hoarding our honey for the long winter of separation.

The day of his going came nearer and I knew he had no time for honey. Even a day. He promised a day away, perhaps a few flowers to press in my memory, to cherish through the winter. The days passed. Until all he could promise was a walk, yes, this evening, a little walk around the dusty streets, dandelions thrusting their ragged clocks through the pavement, all the flowers behind walls and fences in gardens. Too late in the year for honey. But the last day had to be his smallpox injection. Had to be an evening and night of pain and fever and irritation. Had to be a quick peck of farewell, after my breakfast alone. I left him sleeping and came back to winter without honey or flowers. Once. Forever.

Two shapeless old ladies on a hot summer day, prudent in raincoats and headscarves. A wet, happy spaniel between them. He has been swimming in the canal. They pause behind my bench, then one curves back and approaches to sit. I move my bag and she smiles and protests and sits alone. Her huge blue raincoat crackles. She has a worn, humble wedding ring fitted into her plump finger. A grey pigeon with very red feet patters around. A little boy runs and it flutters a little way off. The raincoat pocket rustles and a crumb is tossed. The pigeon gobbles it. More crumbs nearer, and it patters up for them. The woman yells "Hello, Glen!" as the other woman returns. "He's done his job." They go off together and from her other rustling pocket comes something for the smiling dog to crunch.

I am facing the back of the bench, my legs on the wrong side, to catch the sun. The bench backs on to, I face, the tennis courts. Six little boys are lobbing cheap balls back and forth. He always wants to play tennis. I always prefer to sit. Or walk. We play tennis. We've been playing tennis for years. A lifetime of years. Today is what it is like alone. Watching tennis. Watching lives.

A cold wind from the right and the sun from the left, but winter is prevailing in the teeth of the wind.

I have told him we have come to the end. We are finished, have no future, will never dance.

I cannot even remember loving him. Perhaps I didn't. Perhaps the loving is in the folds of the dance, in the enfolding sleep. I cannot love him with the scented dance lingering in my head. Once. Forever.

When I needed him, he left. When I needed letters, there were none. When I was most vulnerable, he spoke of "we" and meant himself and those others who filled my kitchen with dripping boots and axes and cream-cake wrappers and dirty coffee mugs while from behind the door where they were, came the rustling of maps and happy laughter. Since then I have become harder.

It has taken long years for me to become hard enough to tell him that he and I are finished. As if he didn't know. I give him nothing. I tell him nothing. I want nothing from him. I need nothing. Except to be without him. Once. Forever.

But he is fighting back. A lifetime of years ago, even before the tangles, he would not let go. Then we were close enough to fight. He would stand in my room and there would be tears on his cheeks. He would say if you let me go now you will never see me again. I let him go. Every time.

Now, today, he has a bath and says he wants to take me for a meal. Somewhere nice. I don't want to go. We are finished. We go. And he woos me with Margaritas. A lifetime of years too late. Drunk, I teach him the Gay Gordons on the pavement up a sidestreet under the cherry blossom which already is dropping to the ground. A boisterous dizzy dance.

Which he does for the first time at a wedding. He dances with someone else, then, as he comes for me, the band flourishes the final chord. It makes no difference now. And it was the wrong dance.

The last time we made love, the final time, I did not want to. I was in tears. He did not know and I had nowhere to turn for refuge from this pathetic intimacy.

I think he will remember my birthday this year. He usually forgets. It doesn't matter any more.

I used to buy roses for those other anniversaries. The First Meeting. First Sleeping. First Living Together Days. But I was always alone remembering. I don't remember now. I want to forget it all.

I will escape the binding weed. Flee to the solace of the dream of the dance and live there, swaying in his arms in the scented dark, weaving a cocoon of love around ourselves, a perpetual possibility in the languid rhythm of an unending dance. Long ago. Once. Forever.

Valerie Thornton

Annette Berman

Rowan

A kinder season now, no more caging winds;
through the window scarlet rowan, purple slopes,
sing harmony with greens.

I open up the door; there in every flower,
in every night-time star, I find a face
that I could love.

We weather private winters; the sprouting rowan
lost its leaves, but the gentle hills, these solid walls,
I know they will remain.

Last winter, frightened from the dark,
I made a fence with barbs, sharp,
to cut you to the bone;

now, I want it down. Let others come
(as you did before) by an easy path
to an open door.

Inch Cailloch

From Arnold Bocklin's painting *The Island of the Dead*

In the last days we said we would come here;
you the boatman to row me across the narrow
from the burnt bleakness of Conic Hill to the island
tall with black Scots pine; towering shadows
through watery light. The buzzards would be gone
and laden skies would hide the sun.

In that walled place the dead would rise.
MacFarlane and his kin, from unquiet graves,
for one last look (the cool dank place
where garlic grows, a gnarled hill
of blaeberry and heather); the dead would meet the living
and weep for all that they had lost.

In silence, the boatman rows me over
to the island of the dead; feet touch shingle,
the boat pulled up, beached at last
and nothing to do but wait. When it comes
in darkness, flood or fire, the boatman's paid
with all that would be left; a kiss to seal his eyes.

Cailleach Mhor, the Hag of Winter

Now the Hag screams from the shore,
burns tender scrub, stone walls,
where black-faced huddled sheep endure

like stubborn crofts; clutch the hills.
Soon, dying bracken rusts to brown,
stained dark by spattered seedling firs

and wind-blown blemished banks of broom.
Dwarfed by mountains (white reclining bodies
crush; compress a frozen landstrip down)

backed against the wild Atlantic seas,
man grows potatoes, wind-break trees.

Her icy breath sings
bitter songs that wither
she wanders lamenting;

Cailleach Mhor, the Hag of Winter.
Storms hit Mull; her heart is raging,
with the Cuillins behind her

each refuge retreating,
she's touched by the hand of Bride the Maiden
beautiful, lulling, red-haired spring,

and cries, transformed as the black sea-raven,
"I'll come again! I'll come again!"

In the Cafe

With the table between us you casually throw
your coat on mine. The strange remote nearness
contour to contour, press on my mind.

Always something between us? We transcend tables.
But what will they say of forbidden fruits,
of our cryptic words, which rise like question marks?

But to lie down, opened, and brutally lose you;
relinquished into the earth. To give myself up,
when nothing's resolved, to that final act of love?

Spring. Through our cafe window life renews;
strong blades arch, shoot vigorous and fresh from secret ground,
park blossoms nuzzle lovers strolling hand in hand.

Moth

Cocooned in white sheets
at the advent of life
(or death), strung by a tube,
as the wrinkled mask smooths
and thins to fine veins,
when the breathing stops

and you thrash to be free,
I'd expect no rustle of wings.
But you came like an angel
to fill the room; doubtless
the air moved, electric,
around that quiet husk.

Last night, a phantom
with pale velvet wings,
fought the black window
for entrance in; fluttered
on my mirrored lips,
dusted, caressed my eyes.

I turned a page,
found an old belief,
"A spirit of the dead
returns to earth
to visit those they love
...formed as a white moth."

Valerie Gillies

Waterspouts

Who sees the waterspouts drive over the loch
In long succession, and crash in spray on the crags,
Will brave out the storm on the rock ledge
And be watching in the bield of the western slope.

Who hears the waves spout words from their mouths
Exhaled in a breath, and steam blow out and up,
Will hiss when the winds' voices fly through stone cliffs,
Can go through anything, like a shout passes through rocks.

The Rink

The Rink is seen from a distance,
trees in the broch, wall within wall.
A stone clattering down stuns the earth.

You are here on the hill,
you are here with me in silence
encircling the whole summit.

As we are now, they were
leaning over the outer wall in springlight
looking across hills and valleys.

A doe hare comes this way, in no hurry,
not expecting to find humans here,
loping close enough to touch.

Her warm brown back blends
with the feather-grass, her fur
a burr-elm of reds and yellows.

After her come two jack hares,
one solid, one spindly, following her trail
with twists and turns, tides to her moon.

Most marvellous, moving smoothly,
the run of the hares is the lie of the land.
There are times when the creature is a ghost.

We think they have all gone,
till we turn and look behind us:
in the shadow of a shadow

a golden hare rests in the birchwood,
touched thousands and thousands
of times by the sun.

In the Trail of the Wind

Winter midnight
it's been snowing
and the wind's blowing

The horse flings up his head
thoroughbred
born to carry a rider
clear of the fray
he's away

alone in the wild wind
Ericstane cantering
out there
through two gates
jumps the cattlegrid
thunders louder
along the lochside
hoofprints in ice
black script on white

Dark horse in a white night
galloping to the head of the valley
all the way

over the burn
up the back of the farm
by the old tower
where Sir Simon Fraser
rode out to meet
the same fate as the Wallace

A great charger riderless
under the old beech trees
under the high heronry
he circles
with his New Zealand rug on squint
he flaps longlegged night heron

He has run two miles
through the hills
at midnight
Now he spooks at everything
at something in the wind
so close
you just can't see it
ghosting his moonlight flit

Scottish Eclipse

for Sudeep Sen

Are you watching this clear night,
making out the curved edge
of the shadow crossing the moon's disc?
It begins like a bruise, gives her a keeker.

The taxidriver pulls over to the kerb
and we sit gazing together,
clap hands and call out
to help her shrug off the shade.

But the stars grow bigger, stronger,
outshine her. She's not completely gone.
Into the shadow she's stolen
my year in Manasa Gangotri

and she's hidden away
Sudeep's month in Scotland;
in each particular place
one lunar eclipse or two every year.

The moon is always presenting
the same face to earth;
now she glides out to watch us
again, like a silvery third party.

Television

Jane Humphries

Television, the drug of the nation,
breeding ignorance and feeding radiation
The Disposable Heroes of Hiphoprisy

Television, that ubiquitous electronic box which zaps instant entertainment into most Scottish homes makes Scotland, like the rest of the modern world, a tube-obsessed nation. A nation whose cultural image is perpetually constructed and deconstructed by the guardians of our little square friend. Telly addicts are regularly glued to that little box of delights for daily injections of news and current affairs, soap operas and films, game shows and sitcoms. What we choose to tune into, however, is limited to what is on the television menu – a menu which may not be to everyone's taste, least of all women.

Television's role in shaping societal values has been widely debated, from concern over the dissemination of ideas and information which may be politically biased, to the portrayal of one-dimensional characters who reinforce gender, class and racial stereotypes. Those who control the means of television production have a potentially dangerous political force at their disposal, a force which demands scrutiny and criticism from the public because of the influential messages the medium relays. BBC Scotland, STV and Grampian assume a commitment to representing Scottish culture in all its various spheres. There appears, albeit at a superficial level, a healthy realisation that television has an obligation to respond to the heterogeneous, multi-layered fabric of society which makes up contemporary Scotland, both in the mainstream and on the fringe of popular culture.

Or do they? Could it be that television is responsible for continuing to generate inequality through ignorance and misunderstanding of what constitutes a female perspective? Questions have to be asked as to what extent women are being catered for in this television-fixed decade – both in terms of how they are presented on screen, and career opportunities within the industry.

In 1988 Anne Ross Muir wrote an article entitled, 'The Status of Women Working in Film and Television' for a collection of essays called *The Female Gaze*. In the article she stressed that the status of women working in television was usually lower than their male counterparts because an all-boys network existed in every area of the media, which worked against women and denied them entry into the more challenging, creative and lucrative fields. More importantly, women were unable to control the image of how they themselves were being presented.

Because men controlled the industry, it was argued, a masculine frame of reference prevailed on our screens. This had damaging long-term effects for women, as false, unrealistic pictures of what it meant to be a woman were created. One of Muir's major concerns was that until this frame of reference was altered, children of the television generation would be bombarded constantly with a male-biased viewpoint and would grow up under the misconception that there was no other point of view.

There was a great deal of hope expressed in the article also. Muir sensed that, in the late 1980s, there was a growing possibility for change within the media, through a shift in general attitudes resulting from the impact of feminism and the adoption of equal opportunities. Most broadcasting companies agreed (in principle at least, if not in practice), to various recommendations such as job-sharing and flexible working hours.

Her advice at the time was for women to act quickly and take full advantage of the equal opportunity initiatives on offer. In effect women had to do it for themselves and, she argued:

> ...when we have complete access to these important media for self expression and mass communication, when we really share control of the means of production, can we fully establish a 'female gaze' within popular culture and present woman's point of view in all its fascinating multiplicity'.

A decade later it would appear that women in Scotland have taken this advice, and now make up a forceful presence among those shaping the future of Scottish television culture. The names of prodigious female Scottish television presenters spring easily to mind – for a start, the big three, Sheena McDonald, Kirsty Wark and Muriel Grey. All are household names and all present themselves as strong, articulate and intelligent women. Gaining recognition and respect has demanded talent and determination and all three are fine cultural ambassadors, for despite their quintessential diversity, their nationality – Scottish – is a distinctive feature.

"Many things which are considered 'Scottish' characterise me" comments Sheena McDonald. "I try to treat people equally, which I think stems from the old Scottish belief in egalitarianism, and certainly coming from a smaller nation gives the individual a different perspective on world issues. Thus I am aware of the wider picture and try to present a global view. Both these considerations verify my presentation style."

Sheena McDonald epitomises a highly professional, ethical television presenter. The egalitarian myth of the lad, or in this case lass o' pairts, has influenced the person we see on screen, but her progress in the television world has been built on determination, self-belief and careful control of her career path: "I found it difficult to progress as quickly as I wanted to in the early days but I knew I did not want to be caught in the honey trap of the female newsreader. Probably through my family background, I had an inbred sense of justice and never felt patronised, as everyone was treated with equal respect."

Despite her success she believes that the world at large is systematically structured against women, and has experienced her share of male condescention since beginning her career in the media: "Men reading news bulletins tend to gain stature where women are still regarded as pretty mouthpieces. I made a deliberate choice not to get caught in that role. The image you see on the screen is very much me and I tend to think that in the big set-piece political interviews the dynamics are changed for the better because I am a woman. Most politicians are men and often behave like duelling gladiators."

Kirsty Wark is also an ardent fighter for the political rights of the individual to gain representation on television: "I see my job as a privilege and a responsibility. I have, in a sense, to be the voice of the people because I have the opportunity to ask key politicians questions which the ordinary person, by no fault of their own, is unable to do."

Evidence of this style of broadcasting, idealistic and responsible, became apparent in the notorious Thatcher interview. Trying to evade the important political questions and hoping to turn the interview into a 'sisterly' chat Thatcher met more that her match in Wark who, like her interviewee, was not for turning.

Kirsty Wark's attitude to the state of women in broadcasting is very different from Sheena McDonald – she believes positive discrimination is no longer necessary: "I never experienced sexism, though I know certain women have. ...I think doing women-only programmes merely ghettoises the situation."

As a working mother she accepts the pressures that this entails and admits that she is in a fortunate position because she can afford decent child care and has a supportive partner. Now running her own production company with her husband Alan Clements, producing programmes like *Axiom* and *Up Front*, her motivation appears to have evolved into an interest in presenting the political structure of Scottish society.

Lastly there is Muriel Grey, who began her career as mouthpiece for Youth Culture on Tyne Tees' Channel 4 music programme *The Tube* alongside Jools Holland. Outwardly less conventional, her independent production company Gallus Besom challenged mainstream television with highly original programmes like *Walkie Talkie*, the *Munro Show*, and latterly *The Golden Kagoule*. Notoriously outspoken, Muriel Grey challenges preconceived ideas of how women should behave by her upfront, streetwise confrontational interview style. This upbeat image is a welcome alternative to more conventional presenters.

According to Tom Lappin, in an article for the Sunday Times, the run-up to the 1992 general election demonstrated strong evidence to suggest that Scottish women journalists dominated the pre-election coverage. On Scottish was Viv Lumsden, the BBC pulled in Kirsty Wark, Grampian was covered by Anne MacKenzie and Sheena McDonald could be seen on Channel 4's *The World This Week*. Yet he pointed out a significant feature – that this was a fairly recent phenomenon. In the past women presenters were not in evidence and if they were they came against male ribbing and patronising remarks such as the Jane Franchi cut-out doll in the *Naked Radio* team's 'joke' book. The tone of this article was essentially positive, but it seems that despite overall respect for the women in question, they are still challenged aesthetically rather than by their intellectual merits for, as Tom Lappin wrote in the same article:

> What red-blooded Scotsman can deny a secret frisson of excitement as Dewar and Lang, Sillars and Steel are told to 'keep it brief' by any one of them?

This obsession with how women look on screen rather than their journalistic competence is a recurring problem. Many male presenters do not fit into the category of what is pleasing to the female gaze yet they are not under constant criticism over expanding beer guts or receding hair lines. Women who appear in front of the camera are under this added pressure, distressingly, from female as well as male viewers.

During the 1980s Scotland was enjoying a cultural renaissance. The political climate was fertile for women to make their voices heard. Devolution was back on the political horizon, trying to establish the significant difference or 'otherness' Scottish culture offered in contrast to the rest of the United Kingdom; and it would have appeared hypocritical to neglect the gender issue. If Scotland was oppressed as a nation, then Scottish women were doubly oppressed by nationality and gender. One argument as to why women have become more visible is that television produced in Scotland responded to this social change.

While women have been making gains in front of the camera, however, a look behind the scenes reveals a radically different picture. Carol Craig, chair of Equal Opportunities at the BBC highlighted this problem of unequal representation in an article for the *Herald* in February 1993.

Monitoring programmes on the television in Scotland her research project – Action for Women – found evidence to suggest that men still control and dominate the content of what prevails on our screens. For example, when analysing the gender contributions made on *Left Right and Centre* between 1991 and 1992, she discovered that 92% of these were male views. "The reality of this inequality is masked because of the formidable presence of anchorwoman Kirsty Wark". We are fortunate to have such talented women breaking boundaries in television and by their very presence creating role models of high status and ability yet we have to consider that this may distort the reality of deep-rooted gender bias.

In 'Reporting Scotland' the same male bias was discovered. Analysing an item on the public's reaction to last April's budget only one woman to nine men was interviewed, and over a couple of weeks the same programme used 80% more contributions from men. It appears that women simply are not being given equal access to express their views on air.

It is not just the ratio of men to women which is problematic but that when women are interviewed their role appears much more limited. They are not called upon as specialists but merely involved in passive roles.

In other areas apart from hard core news the same sad story unfolds. Televised sport is heavily male-biased as only two per cent of it is devoted to women's sport or sportswomen. Again the presence of Hazel Irvine in the studio cloaks the actual inequality. In areas traditionally considered 'female', such as arts and drama, the situation is also less favourable to women. For example on the *Play On One* series for BBC Scotland only three out of twenty-four plays were written by women.

Carol Craig comments that the BBC in particular is aware that its programmes should reflect the composition and diversity of its audience, yet her research indicates that this is not really happening.

Apart from this revealing piece of qualitative research, one of the main problems in exposing the difficulties for women in this area is that access to data on the actual positions women hold in television and in what job areas they occupy is very hard to obtain. Watching the credits roll it becomes obvious that women are certainly conspicuous by their absence in technical areas such as sound, camera and engineering. There is no easy answer how to resolve this situation apart from education and increased training schemes but with the depressed state of workshops and funding this is proving increasingly more difficult.

The Broadcasting, Entertainers, Cinematography and Theatre Union (BECTU) was unable to produce any breakdown of affiliated members with which to gauge the status of women in the industry, and although women are working outside the mainstream in independent production companies, power at senior management level is very much in male hands:

BBC Senior Management

Controller – John McCormick
Head of TV – Colin Cameron
Radio – James Boyle
Corporate Affairs – Fiona Hamill
Finance – Bryan Mitchell
Engineering – Grant McWilliam
Resources – Andy Davy

STV Senior Management

Managing Director – Gus Macdonald
Director of Finance – Duncan Kinloch
Broadcasting – Eileen Gallagher
Resources – Harry Urquhart

Because men hold the decision-making roles, it is their views that dominate programming. With the majority of senior positions occupied by men, a hierarchy of male terms of reference is constructed which often marginalises or elides women's interests. At lower levels of management women are slowly moving up the ladder, but it is steep and heavily rigged to favour men. Change is a gradual process and it is up to women to try and initiate positive action in order to change their position in the future.

Scottish Women was a programme which genuinely created a forum for women to express their views. The programme was the brainchild of Gus Macdonald and evolved from a programme called *Granada 500* (created as a political platform to voice Scottish opinion on issues like Devolution). Realising that women were not given the chance to speak out on television, Gus Macdonald adapted the format into *One Hundred Scottish Women*. It was a radical idea, based around a debate with the facility of a voting panel so those participating could actively express their preferences. The audience was comprised of one hundred MORI-selected women, resulting in an across-the-board sample of women living in Scotland and this added authenticity to the resulting findings. Hosted admirably by Sheena McDonald, here was the first real opportunity for women to discuss and analyse issues from a female viewpoint.

In an arena far from the usual Westminster style, the programme illustrated the rich diversity of female culture and that women were articulate and opinionated. There was nothing contrived or aggressive about the way the programme was hosted and it gave women a chance to talk candidly from their individual experience. This open discussion was encouraging and liberating for both men and women proving that radical, vital programme-making could attract audience ratings.

The current *Scottish Women* has lost much of this revolutionary zeal by changing the format into a more conventional chat show. The audience is now carefully researched and a panel of 'experts' are included to comment on the various subjects chosen for discussion. This changes the whole dynamic of the programme by creating a division whereby the panel appear to be more learned than the audience.

Now billed as a pseudo-Oprah Winfrey type 'show', surely the title *Scottish Women* is a misnomer, as the inclusion of men and the introduction of a panel puts a tighter gag on the voices of those whom the programme is aimed at – women. This is not to say that *Scottish Women* should be exclusively for women but the programme has now lost its political edge and is just another cheap attempt at providing entertainment and audience ratings in the guise of a women-friendly programme.

It is a formative time for presenter Kaye Adams, but dashing around like Kilroy Silk making patronising innuendoes at the expense of the audience verges on tabloid sensationalism. If this is the future for programmes aimed at a female audience we are certainly moving backwards. But at least the programme still exists and may subsequently improve.

Censoring the visual gaze into a purely politically-correct format is an approach which negates our right to free choice, self determination and critical thinking and is not the answer. In a time when we, as viewing consumers, have a greater choice from commercial television from cable and satellite, there is no real choice if the types of programmes on offer to us are by and large more of the same. If this is the case, less is more. There has to be more responsibility and an awareness of the need to represent minority interests from those holding the power.

As tax payers, television license holders and a viewing audience, women, hardly a minority, have a right to demand that they are included in every aspect of television coverage from news to drama, and that the rich diversity of female images are presented in a realistic and non-sexist manner.

Conspiracy theorists may claim that there is a deliberate ploy to exclude women from key roles in television, but the reality is that many men are supportive of women's rights and are aware that 52% of the Scottish population deserve a fair and equal voice. Previous writers on the subject of women's roles in Scottish Television/Media have argued that it is up to women to see that the situation is improved. However, the future is not entirely in our hands. Until there is no need to talk about women's position as 'other' to men in any institution, and until we have gained the rights we have demanded in education, childcare, promotion and pay, it will remain a flaming issue.

Jane Humphries

Morelle Smith

The Old Straight Track

No downtown, no warehouses,
no stacked and boarded
piled-up or discarded
feelings. No long shelf-life
emotions. Retrieval of the
sun, walking through forgotten passages;
perhaps its autumn
that returns the players to the stage –
the audience back to their seats –
and time returns to me.

Perhaps it was the sea-journeys,
perhaps the standing stones.
Perhaps it was the tree-lined roads
I travelled on, alone.

Light filters through a path
of trees; lights up the passages
of once-walked time.
I am an avenue of memories
standing in a single morning
sunlit, saturate with time.

Playing the Sun

Well after dawn
The fiddle player
Slips his instrument into the case,
So easily I hardly notice it.

Dance brings dawn
And I climb slow frets
To work on the loose tangles
Of the toppling stars that
Tilt to the horizon, from exhaustion.

Play me the night, I say
And he lifts his head,
Dizzy with creation,
and I slip between him and the fiddle
Pull dawn blanket over us
and go hunting in and out
Of the retreating stars.

This has to be a dream he says
And I touch his fingers
With a horse-hair bow.
He shudders into daylight,
Dawn-strung, among the rafters
Of the night's rebellion.

– We should be asleep at night,
We should be –
– Wake, wake, I tune him
Into fingers of a dream,
Pulling music-ribbons
from the distant mirrors of the stars.
They echo back the fiddler's tune.
– Listen! I say.
We hear the night replaying,
Softly, as we run our
Fiddle-fingers over skin.

I lie beside the fiddler,
Unpicking his music –
Threads pulled across us,
Like a blanket –
Weaving fast night, plucking quick feathers –
Holding night and music,
Waking up and dying endlessly –
Hurtling round the sun-track
In this embrace of fire.

Boatman

While I spoke to him
The owner of the boats
Passed a thin rope through his hands
As if to tie up all loose ends,
Dispense forever with a thread
That had uncertain destinations
And might lead to something
Coiled beneath his memory
Like a sleeping snake.
He talked as if such memories
Could be appeased, could be coerced
To go on sleeping
Only while he spoke.

His face was brown and bearded
And his eyes spent so long looking
Into distance that when he
Brought them back to me,
They were sea-stained,
Like reflections of the sky.

I found a shell beside the path
that led down to the boathouse.
He looked as though he had a tale to tell
But there was no one he could tell it to,
No one who knew the sea
As well as he did,
No one he could trust with his sea-eyes –
– Half Russian, he said,
'With bits of Welsh and Irish' –

He coiled his rope and talked of boats
And held us in contempt
For all we did not know.
His story lay like a beached sail,
Waiting for high tide.
His eyes blurted out horizons,
As he looked out past the jetty,
Out to the open sea.

– Once you get a taste for it
It will not let you go.

I thought that he was talking
Of the sea of course,
But when his eyes swung round
To look at me
I felt I did not know at all
What he was meaning
And I held my sea-shell
In my hand and turned to go
And felt the coiled rope circle
Like an undertow and still –
Felt that I did not know.

Honor Patching

Fossil Sand-Ripples

300 million years
Since the sea nudged
The sand and rucked it,
Left it pleated, ridged.

Finding its shape
Each ripple learned
To fit the next one,
The sand's skin turned

To a long thrill
Of peaks and hollows,
Answering the swell.
Now, in the shallows,

Sand as cold
And hard as bone,
But your touch printed
In ripples on my skin.

Old tides, old loves,
Patterned and delicate,
I trace their secret,
Their ribs and curves.

On The Dundee Bus

We hang in this bus like herrings in the smoke,
Elbow to elbow, as though the whole of Fife
Were travelling, pickled in ammoniac reek
Of babies' nappies. Twisting, I rub a sleeve
Against the window where I'm crammed. Misted
Glass smears, I glimpse a blur of trees,
Craning my neck beneath *No Smoking* pasted
At eye-height. Across the Tay, Dundee's
Blue-wet runs, smudges smoke and sky.
Rust-red, an oil-rig wades against the water's
Metal. A wide light runs frosty
Clear to the river. Like mothers and daughters
in damp headscarves, lapwings land, all
A-flutter, to probe for worms, their scraps of scandal.

Roberta ShoafEnge

Wordgames

The answer lay on the floor
  in scattered invisible letters.

Drama! she lamented. Where's the fire
  and drama?
Well, it never had been there, had it?
  She never gave me the D.

You know, she said, it's like being married to
  your brother. It's... like... incest.
We both found that amusing, and she toyed
  with the I for a while before handing it over.

I just *couldn't* leave him – he's so
  vulnerable – so very, very vulnerable.
The V she kept,
  unwilling to give it up.

We talked about "the big O". She thought she
  remembered it, but wasn't exactly sure.
We bounced the O around on the walls,
  then let it roll away.

She argued his finer points: Reliability,
  Rationality, Reason.
Admirable qualities, we agreed.
  (Neither of us wanted the R).

It's the uncertainty, she explained – if only I were
  absolutely certain.
She wavered for a long time. I had to take
  the C from her.

She looked around.
  I had the E.
Empathy was my only contribution
  to this awkward mess.

So.
  There were all the letters.
She wanted to mix them up,
  and somehow
    make a different word.

Scaffolding

Outside the hospital window
brackets grip steel-pipe crutches
in a prosthetic metal mesh, creating this

futile support system, surrounding the
tottering building, desperately
trying to bear the weight of

a crippled structure with atrophied walls,
cataract windows, hunchbacked floors
and a balding roof while

special consultants, after considered diagnosis,
attend to ageing parts,
cutting, replacing and splinting because

councillors deny the building's state of ill-health
and protest against the end of its useful life
It just needs a few repairs.

Inside a smell of rusting bodies;
crumbling bits of broken joints, leaky
tracts and unstable hearts, repaired with

steel pins and drills, double-glazed pills,
held together with tape and tubes
surveyed with monitors which are all just

temporary measures and the foreman apologises for
the mess he's created, but it will all be cleared up
just as soon as I'm fixed which

he assures me will be very soon as he whispers
to my family about the extent of the damage to the
exterior and interior and guarantees his work but

my thin daughter and her tense husband worry and pace
Do you think she can hear us?
She just keeps staring out the window.

Please, please take the scaffolding down.
The building is too old to stand.

Sex Education

They told us how it worked,
  sex.
Sex makes babies.

They told us how the sperm
  resolutely gravitates
    to the waiting, willing egg
      and conception occurs.
They told us how the bundle of cells
  glides effortlessly
    down the tube
      to nestle in the plush womb.
They told us how for nine months
  the embryo grows
    into a foetus
      with tiny arms and legs.
They told us how at birth
  an oblong head followed by
    a sticky pink body emerges,
      screaming for air.

But they didn't tell us about the blood.

They didn't tell us about the blood
  that without oxygen looks blue,
    blue like the baby with the cord
      lynched around its neck
They didn't tell us about the blood
  that in the third month
    comes out in coagulated knots
      with a lumpy mass attached.
They didn't tell us about the blood
  that explodes from the tube,
    filling the belly with gore
      rushing up to suffocate the heart.
They didn't tell us about the blood
  that comes every month
    with raging regularity
      mocking our hopes.

Purple

Sylvia G Pearson

Debbie sat on the couch opposite her father and pulled bits of yellowed foam from a gash in one of the arms. Her eyes flitted from his face to the door and then back again. He was making a roll-up, but his hands were shaking, and most of the tobacco shreds were falling on to his knee. She watched him brush them off on to their tobacco-coloured carpet.

In the far corner of the room Billy, her wee brother, was trying to birl a wheel of his buggy, but it was buckled. He gave up and turned his attention to a toy police car. "Eee-awe-eee-awe-eee-awe".

"Away an see if that bloody ambulance is comin yet", her dad growled, not looking up.

Debbie slid off the couch and ran to the door. It was frosty outside, and some puddles had ice on them. She felt the cold strike the bare bit between her jeans and top. By putting one foot in a hole in the wire netting she could hoist herself up to lean over the gate. She swung back and forth on it a few times, glanced up and down the street, and then decided that she would like another look at her mum.

There was a terrible smell of sick and bevvy in the bedroom. Her mum's eyes were closed, face all purple and red blotches. She still had her clothes on. Her hair was wild, matted, and she was moaning. Wee bubbles were going in and out of her blue lips. One of her shoes was on the floor, the other nowhere to be seen.

"Any sign o that ambulance, *you*?" shouted her dad, starting to cough and wheeze. Debbie ran to the living-room door. "No yet, dad – d'ye want a drink i juice or somethin – there's a wee drop red Kola in the cubburd?" she asked, desperate to keep him calm, trying to hold back her tears, not wanting to make him angry.

"Naw! Ah jist want the ambulance tae come an take that cow *away*!"

Debbie chewed at her bottom lip. How long would they keep her mum this time? Would she come back all nice and clean and sensible and smelling of soap – like the other times? And would she say, smiling and taking Debbie on her knee, "That's me finished this time, doll, nae mair bevvy fur yours truly. Things is gonnae be different fae noo on. We're gonnae get yer room aw done up pink an purple like ah sayed, an a new suite, an bunk beds fur you an Billy, an new shoes fur the school ...*An* we'll get yer ears pierced fur yer burthday!"

And then, would the fighting start all over again, with her dad out every night with his pals, and her mum sitting in that old dressing gown drinking gold cans of Carlsberg Special like the ones on the telly ads – and herself and Billy eating squares of red jelly, and tinned soup, and toast?

She stood beside the bed, gaze fixed on her mother's hands – chipped varnish, dirt under the nails. Two buttons of her mum's blouse were undone. Carefully, holding her breath, Debbie reached out over the big breasts, each one slopping sideways, and slipped the loops over two white pearls. Her mother grunted, drew an arm across her face as though brushing a fly away. The pearls popped out again.

It was her mum's best blouse – purple. She *loved* purple. Once when Debbie's dad was dead drunk on the couch she had stolen a fistful of coins from his pocket and bought a wee pot of African violets from the shop on the corner. It was her mum's birthday next day, and she went crazy about the flowers. Debbie gave them to her before breakfast – before she started drinking, so that she could enjoy the look on her face. It was *magic*!

There was a sharp knock on the door. "See if that's the ambulance", shouted her father, but Debbie knew it couldn't be – she would have heard it coming into the street. She raced to the door anyway. It was Lorna, the social worker. Debbie liked her the best out of the whole lot because she never made her mother cry, and she never made her dad walk out the door.

"It's Lorna, Dad. She's got a buggy for Billy. It's a blue yin."

"Hi, Debbie. Can I come in? Mum at the shops?"

"Naw, ma ma's no well. She's in 'er bed. We're waitin on the ambulance. The doaktur's been. He says it's her stummik again. She'll huff tae get it cleaned oot, but jist come in. It's awright, ma dad's in."

Debbie closed the door behind the social worker, and followed her into the living room. Lorna didn't sit down. Billy jumped across to look at his new buggy, and plonked himself in it as soon as it was opened out. Lorna looked very serious and was asking her dad if their Aunty Josie would be taking the children as usual.

"Is something gonnae happen tae ma ma, Lorna?" asked Debbie, on the verge of tears. D'ye want tae see 'er? She's in 'er bed."

"Gie the lassie peace fur Goad's sake", hissed her dad, chucking a match into the empty fireplace.

"It's all right, William, I don't mind. I think Debbie wants me to."

"Suit yersel!"

Lorna stood at the foot of the bed and stared. "Why are you asking me if something's going to happen to your mum, Debbie?"

The girl thought for a moment, chewing her lip again. "We-e-ell, ...sometimes when ma ma's on the bevvy an she's greetin, she says tae me 'now lissen, Debbie, if anythin ever happens to me you're tae get ma purple ring' ...an she says it over an over again – 'now mind, Debbie, you're tae get that purple ring, it used tae be yer nanna's' ...*see* – Ah'll show ye. It's in a wee red boax in the top drawer."

She clambered on to a chair, rummaged through a jumble of clothes, and finally jumped down with the amethyst ring on her thumb.

Lorna was smiling, but it wasn't her usual smile. "So... was Mum on the Carlsbergs yesterday, Debbie?"

"Naw, it wisnae the Carlsbug Speshuwls. It wiz somethin else. Ma dad sayed it wiz rubbish stuff. She wiz awffy seeck efter it. It wiz in a wee bottle – like a meddissin bottle – but clear glass. You could see the colour – it wiz purple, jist like the ring." Debbie held it up to the light. "It's a *magic* colour, eh Lorna – ma ma's favritt."

Sylvia G Pearson

Jenny Robertson

The Pattern

I hold a brown-veined autumn leaf.
a rose, a petal,
the patterning of growth and grief;
midwinter reft and dearth;
midnight vigil,
hope asleep; and feel
warmth beyond the snow,
a hidden path, lantern glow.

December 25th

From our window level with tree tops
I watch a brief December day
fade behind black branches.

Crows clamour – dark shapes – about a golden dome.

(A world away cities are sated with commerce
called, too crudely, Christmas.)

The tide of light has turned
with the midwinter solstice.

This frozen land is fasting;
its ill-lit streets poor showcases
for goods guarded as once the Czar's gold glitter:

a feast enticing – distant

as stars from a stable door.

Son of Man

His face is crowned with candleshine,
solemnity of soaring voices,
the incense word: *Pomiluj.*

He is slumped in dust
of six million trampling feet,
hat of rabbit fur askew.

Out of town we glimpse him among birches –
those naked Russian darlings –
reaching from thawing earth to distant blue.

Dark pines praise him,
bowed beneath April snow.

His is in the faces
of shawled women,
whose eyes suffer, bloodshot, bruised.

As well as in laughter of lovers
and children, swaddled like bundles
in soul-less cities, shabby and subdued.

Unicorn

(a reply to a far-from-*ofishial* herring, George Gunn)

No eagle poised on straining wings,
brash and bronze against the grey
sweep of rainwashed skies;
bleat of new-dropped lambs:

Scotland's symbol is the unicorn:
a beast of dream, ox-strong and slim,
whose creamy shoulders broke an early dawn
before walls were raised or makars born.

A beast of fable with its single horn,
fey and fearsome; yet will come
to a girl's untutored song,
lay its crested head, like blossom, down:

a gentle guardian of frailty,
dumb as moonlight, potent, free.

The Diary of Perpetua (c202 A.D.)

(Vibia Perpetua, a twenty-year-old mother, breast-feeding her child, was arrested for civil disobedience. She and her friends, including her pregnant slave, Felicitas, refused to perform the ritual for the Emperor's welfare and were sentenced to fight with beasts in the arena – a wild cow was sent against the two women.)

1. Choice

My family bring violets,
weeping, heart-wrung pleas;
call me atheist, unnatural, strange.
I cannot change,
no, not for violets,
or memories of shadowed grass,
of birdsong, blossom, spring;
not even for my little son
– oh, nurse him well!

You say, abjure that impious braggart
dragging wretched wood, that slave,
his empty title slung around his neck.
But I say laurel wreaths
are mere profanities.
So do not tempt me now
with tears, or petals
soft as my baby's skin.

The bowstring of my choice is fully drawn.
Like a runner, stripped, oiled,
I speed arrow-swift towards my prize
and only angels hear my feathers sing.

2. Her first prison dream

I entered a garden
  filled with light,
with many thousands gathered,
  dressed in white;
and, milking sheep, a pale-haired shepherd
  fed his lambs.
His garb was coarse, his welcome kind:
  "Child, come!"
He put some cheese into my hands:
  "Daughter, eat!"
I ate the cheese the shepherd offered.
  Its taste was sweet.
And, when I awoke, I still felt sweetness
  on my breath.
At once I called my brother to me:
  "It will be death."
From then we hoped no more for pleasure
  in this life;
instead, having tasted heaven
  I found health,
and though my father would not let me nurse my child
  my breasts were not sore,
nor was I tormented with worry for him:
  I hurt no more.

3. She dreams she fights the fiend

I head knocking, urgent, loud,
the prison gates opened. I went
over rough rocks to a vast arena,
an astounded crowd, and wondered,

why no wild beasts were let loose;
heard a voice: "I shall share your fight."

I looked around. Who spoke?

And now I saw my opponent:
no wild beast this, but a man, hideous, huge,
with fighting men beside him. I had companions too,
young men who stripped and oiled me.
I knew no shame, for I became a man.

And now the Master appeared, so tall he towered
above the amphitheatre. He wore the purple,
and his sandals were trimmed with silver, tied with gold.
He bore a green bough laden with golden apples:
"This will be her prize. Fight now."

And so combat was joined. I struck his face with my heels,
felt myself airborne, began to strike. He fell.
I trampled him to shouts of triumph, victory songs.
Then the Master took my face between his hands:
"Daughter, peace!" I received his kiss, received
the apple bough: and woke.

Thus I knew my fight will not be against the fiend –
but I know who will win!

I have recorded the main events since our arrest.
I cannot record the contest. If anyone
wishes to do so, let it be done!

4. The Emperor's Games

Mother, Virgin, you wove in your womb
    from purple silk
the robe of love made weak and poor:
    have mercy now.

Master, we dare not enter your chamber
    clad in rags:
O, Bridegroom, surpassing beauty,
    clothe us with suffering.

O, blessed feet, O purest harlot's kiss,
    the prostitute exchanged
her costly perfume for more precious myrrh:
    and knew no shame.

Behold, the feast is served, the Bridegroom waits.
    Leave dungeon, chains.
We run, dazzled, between cheers and roars
    to claim our prize.

Jenni Daiches

Leaving Scotland

The plough and the harvester have etched
the land. Its quilted particularity
needle-sharp, its colours filling
the heart. Umber, tender brown,
moleskin, fox red, bracken and barley.
The earth falls. I am on my way.

The *Hector* drawn
by the sun out of the mouth
of Loch Broom, servant
to the winds. Her ribs
enter the bodies
of the two hundred. The ocean
shivers their thin dreams,
the spray's hiss tears
the words on their tongues.
They have hardly begun.

We tilt into cloud that blurs one part
of my world. Leaving that land's lack
of grace, its spitting discord, water
on hot coals. The sky opens.
A thousand wonders disclosed, loch
and mountain, radical alchemy of rock
and light, fusion of limit and distance.

It has ended.
Each generation grafted
to soil, to sea loch, to river.
The wake of the *Hector*
furrows their love, the sails
heavy as grief. Eyes
follow a path from the east.

Leaving the cryptic city, the boy
begging at the steps, effulgent minds
dulled by crack and drink, women
dancing together to the music of men.

Blown far to the north,
beaten to Newfoundland,
then hirpling south
to the crooked finger
that was named Nova Scotia.
They have cattle and ploughs.

> They have oatmeal for the first winter
> which waits, a wolf
> beyond the ring of fire.
> They have axes and scar
> their hands with the felling of trees.
> The *Hector* escapes the roar
> of Arctic ice.

Niagara below me, a glittering palace
of spindrift. We prepare the return to earth
and curve over the shore of the great
lake. I walk in another city
and find Scotland in the necropolis,
the proof roughly cut in stone.
The evening sun splinters a rowan
into a myriad monarch butterflies.
Below this prism of lustrous red
on red I read the abradant past.

> They hack into the dark
> forest under the dying
> leaves. As they draw sap
> from the maple and fish
> from the water Gaelic unwinds
> from their lips. Song
> spills and runs.
> A young man wraps his plaid
> on his arm and kills
> a deer in the snow.
> The blood warms him.

Geese skein on the burning tail
of August. The road is a hundred miles
of wheat stubble, the huge barns
shelter a year's labour. On and on.
Leaving the learning of stone on a dyke,
and the plough that heals the battlefield.
The *Hector*'s two hundred never return.
They send home for granite to build.

Running at dusk

Water dull as pewter
tarnishes the sand. Hound's
Point lights cluster like snow-
berries. Strung along
the bridge coral beacons
split into crystals.

I run for home.
Night breathes at my neck.
All day gulls have screamed
as if to lash the storm to life.

Bats flick from the trees
like flints from a catapult.
The sky is thumb-brushed
with angry rose. I'm running,
past the burn that underscores
the wind, the thorn forked
as tongues. The firth
shakes the pebbles at its rim.

The dark begins to howl.
Past the windows blank as screens,
sweat hot on my back, air ice
in my lungs, the day,
the road, the bridge, beyond my sight.

Jewish Cemetery, Frankfurt

Deep autumnal green has soaked the earth.
Through the barred gate it invites like velvet,
beckons an intrusion under the awkward
arms of the broad old trees, boldly red,
frailly yellow as a night's alluring moon.
The wall is also old, its rough centuries warm
to the hand. The people passing would think it odd
if a woman rested her head against it and wept.
The trees are helpless within the spiralled leaves.
Beyond are the stones, huddled, dark, leaning
to the right, the left, forward, shawled in the light
of a lenient afternoon. Their faces void,
their grey garments folded close. I listen.
I believe there's a thread of ancient sound. The city
takes a breath. The trams, the river traffic, the market
stalls, dissolve. I smell the fire and the blood,
the acrid smoke of fear. Where once a temple
stood some simple words confine catastrophe.
If only I had love enough for all.

Reviews

Castles in the Air

The Celts, Malcolm Chapman, St Martin's Press, £45; *Poem, Purpose and Place*, Colin Nicholson, Polygon, £11.95; *Identifying Poets*, Robert Crawford, EUP, £25

Construction is a fashionable word in literary criticism these days, and these three books concern themselves in different ways with construction – the material with which the Celtic, and more particularly Scottish, identity has been articulated either by others (in Chapman's case) or by artists working within the community.

In *The Celts,* Malcolm Chapman brings a social anthropologist's tools to bear on a dauntingly complex subject, beginning with the Greek and Roman cultures which gave us the words *keltoi* and *galatae*, pointing out that the ancient Greek *kelton ethnos* translates not so much as 'the Celtic people' but rather 'white trash' or something of the kind. In other words, the *keltoi* were not so much a defined group of people as something that the Greeks *were not.* This theme of 'otherness' has permeated Celtic history and accounts for why people as different physically and temperamentally as, for example, the Welsh and the Irish came to be regarded as a 'Celtic' entity.

In setting about the dissection of centuries' accretion of myth Chapman focuses on two communities in particular: the Breton and the Scottish, concentrating on the complex relationship between centre and periphery which is the mechanism that drives the accretion process:

> The periphery may seem, if intermittently inspected, to be a repository of timeless custom, but this is only an artifact of a mode of observation; a discourse of the past surrounds the periphery, making it easy to suppose that the periphery is outside of time, and changeless.

Bagpipes are a good example: once common throughout Europe, fashion at the centre moved on to newer instruments and the bagpipes, or rather the imitation of bagpipes by composers such as Handel and Corelli in the eighteenth century, were instantly recognised by audiences as a symbol of rural simplicity. Chapman examines this and other manifestations of the same phenomenon, taking into account too the corresponding tendency for 'the other' to contribute to this process of myth-making. As he says of the 1988 Channel 4 Series *The Blood is Strong*: "A typical highly-selective prejudiced misinformed self-congratulatory historiography and history of the Scottish Highlands, bulging with vicarious grievance". Strong words, carrying the implication that behind Chapman's call to 'get real' is a call to accept a political reality which is genuinely foreign (something with which the Pictish element in Scotland would no doubt agree). For all that, *The Celts* is an absorbing survey of Scottish and Celtic social history, language, and interaction.

In his introduction to *Poem, Purpose and Place*, Colin Nicholson hints that his purpose is to assemble from the work of his subjects a picture of Scottish identity. Indeed the book's subtitle is *Shaping Identity in Contemporary Scottish Verse*. In a series of interviews with fourteen 'senior' poets a picture emerges, though not so much in the coherent manner of a thesis as by implication. If this is a criticism, it is more a suggestion of confusion over its *raison d'être* than cavilling with its content. As the introduction points out, a prime purpose of the book is to provide an introduction to the work of the poets therein for students in particular, and for the interested non-Scot in general.

In these terms the book works well, giving enough space to go into some depth (more so with some writers than others). For someone like Douglas Dunn, whose work I have in the past found difficult to appreciate, Nicholson's sketch was particularly useful. The technique of conducting an interview and interpolating the poet's answers with critical comment and extracts rather than formal questions is a well-made balance between the academic and the conversational, and has the added advantage of negotiating that difficult area between what writers believe themselves to be communicating and what the reader perceives their message to be. That said, the technique also highlights the benefits and the drawbacks a country like Scotland has for critics: on the one hand it is possible to be familiar in personal terms with all the writers; on the other, that familiarity can seem to compromise objectivity. In literary terms, of course, objectivity is a construction. In this case, arguably, resembling a cosy bungalow with big bad wolves like Tom Leonard or Tom Scott huffing and puffing outside.

Related to this sense of cosiness is the sense that Lyotard's image, cited in the introduction, of writers being members of a kind of friendly society to which they contribute their work in return for interest, is allowed to pass to easily. It is certainly true that artists, and particuarly writers, have an important role to play in defining society, but they are also the people outside the tent, spitting in. To understand how writers shape identity it is necessary to address this side of the equation too.

Nonetheless, two important themes stand out among the chosen writers: one is a strong element of autodidacticism, the other, something of an antisyzygy, a wry reflection on Dana Gioia's remark, discussed by William Neill in *Chapman* 72, to the effect that it is necessary, to be a writer in the USA, to have a Master's degree in creative writing. It's noticeable how many of the fourteen interviewees in *Poem, Purpose and Place* are, or have been, schoolteachers, as though the corresponding qualification here is a B.Ed or a PGCE. Underlying that flip observation is an important point about the place of the writer in Scottish society: arguably the poet as teacher is a throwback to the mythical bard, *pace* Malcolm Chapman, a living Celtic tradition that is real and valid.

Superficially, Robert Crawford's *Identifying Poets* is a similar book to Nicholson's, containing as it does a series of essays on a variety of poets. But where *Poem, Purpose and Place* is essentially a textbook, a reference work, *Identifying Poets* is theory good and proper. In it Crawford seeks to define the species 'identifying poet', basing his argument in the work of Mikahail Bakhtin, particularly the Russian's interest in dialogue, in the multiple voices of a single author.

Crawford argues that 'home' is the dominant theme of contemporary poetry, but more importantly, the poets he discusses are shown to be engaged in constructing a territorial identity out of language. The opening essay, on Robert Frost, or 'Robert Frosts', exemplifies the approach: Crawford analyses the various guises Frost adopted during his career, the interest in archaeology, native American culture and the image of the farmer-poet in particular, and demonstrates how these can be seen as constructions. For example, Frost used the word 'farmer' when, in England, he was in reality looking after a garden. Rather than using his analytical tools to undermine a reputation, Crawford uses them to celebrate the internal dialogue Frost conducts. The following essays, on MacDiarmid, MacGill-Eain, Murray, Ashbery, Kuppner and Home (as in the *graffito* "I thought Home was a Tory ex-prime minister until I discovered squatting") share the opening essay's sense of relish.

In MacDiarmid the principle of internal dialogue is shown at its clearest:

> ...his achievement in *A Drunk Man* of a classic examination of the Scottish psyche is made possible precisely because he was not content to remain within the confines of the existing Scottish literary consciousness. His triumph was to go beyond that by going outside it, then returning with foreign elements in order to rebuild and expand that Scottish literary consciousness using the most recent and most ambitious imported materials.

This is an important argument, since it is saying in effect that to know a territory's boundary and have a proactive relationship with that territory, it is necessary to conduct a dialogue with what lies beyond it – essentially a statement of Crawford's own position. Although in his introduction he modestly describes the book as having 'a Scottish flavour', the Scottish element is a lot stronger than that. Crawford is plainly constructing an identity for himself that has curious parallels with MacDiarmid in both the construction process and resultant edifice. Indeed, I can imagine a future student penning a thesis on MacDiarmid and Crawford, the Russian connection being one point of departure, the shadowy figure of Eliot (a strong, underexplored presence in *Identifying Poets*) lurking in the background another. After all, MacDiarmid and Crawford share an ambitiousness that, whether it transcends the merely personal or not, certainly stirs dull roots of animus among those outside their respective circles.

Crawford shows an unexpected appetite for fun, a delight in both the academic perscrutation of difficult texts, and also in the more demotic, though no less intelligent, humour of Ashbery and Kuppner. The latter is a particularly surprising inclusion, and if Crawford's argument at this point seems a bit tangental, Kuppner's work successfully illustrates the complexity of the modern linguistic/poetic world.

If *Identifying Poets* has a flaw, it lies in a courteous reluctance to engage in debate with the Scottish element in the book which contrasts most strikingly with the chapter on Les Murray in particular, where Crawford draws parallels with Judith Wright that he himself points out may be thought inflammatory in Australia. Also, while the thesis is completely non-sexist, the praxis is almost exclusively based on male examples – Judith Wright is a dialogic element in the discussion of Murray and not present in her own right. Given that the theory is a construction, I'd have thought it would be possible to build in a female dimension without too much trouble.

These cavils apart, *Identifying Poets* is a critical *tour de force*. The old certainties become less and less adequate in dealing with an increasingly complex and deceitful world, and new critical tools are vital in the broadest sense if we humble mortals are to enjoy an adult relationship with those who govern us. *Identifying Poets* is not an easy read by any means, but well worth the effort, and in the stolid castle that is the world of Scottish criticism, a breath of fresh air. *Peter Cudmore*

The Owl of Minerva

Virtue, Learning and the Scottish Enlightenment, David Allan, EUP, £45/£18.95; *A History of the Church of Scotland 1660–1679*, James Kirkton, Edwin Mellen Press, £39.95; *An Enlightened Scot: Hugh Cleghorn, 1752–1837*, Aylwyn Clark, Black Ace Books, £19.95

As Hegel put it, "the owl of Minerva spreads its wings only at dusk", by which he meant that history moves in such a way that wisdom comes about only near the end of a historical cycle. In *Virtue, Learning and the Scottish Enlightenment*, David Allan argues, in truly Hegelian spirit, that the Enlightenment in Scotland did not suddenly flourish in the eighteenth century after nearly two centuries of religious bigotry and fanaticism, as has been assumed by many influential historians, perhaps most notoriously by Hugh Trevor-Roper. Rather, he demonstrates that such luminaries as David Hume, Adam Ferguson and Lord Kames far from making a radical break with the past actually owed much to their predecessors, who included Renaissance humanists like George Buchanan, and even theological dogmatists like John Knox and Andrew Melville. Allan treats the Scottish Enlightenment not so much as the dawn of modern Scotland, but as the twilight of certain kinds of discourse which began during the Reformation. The Enlightenment in Scotland, as in the rest of pre-Napoleonic Europe (though Allan has little to say about the European Enlightenment), signified the end of Renaissance humanism, indeed its final flowering before the onset of industrialisation and mass society.

Allan's book is subtitled *Ideas of Scholarship in Early Modern History* because he makes it evident that historical writing of the period provides the key to understanding the continuum between the Age of the Covenanters and the Age of Enlightenment, the Reformation itself a kind of "big bang". What these diverse periods have in common is that historical writing was very important in each one, beginning with Buchanan's *History of Scotland* (1582), originally written in Latin, and translated by J Fraser in 1690. If we turn to the Enlightenment period itself, even David Hume was much more widely read as the author of *The History of England* than of *A Treatise of Human Nature*, though it is the latter which has gained him immortality as a philosopher.

Historical writing was so central to Scottish culture since the Reformation because historians investigated more thoroughly than anyone else how virtue, learning and political leadership should inter-relate in order to bring about a better society. At first they did so in religious (particularly Calvinist) terms, but later on in purely secular language. "Secular", however, tended to be a relative term in the Enlightenment. The most prominent "enlightened" Scottish historian, William Robertson, for example, famous throughout Europe for his histories of Scotland, America and the Emperor Charles V, was also a moderator of the Church of Scotland. The urgency of the debate about virtue, learning and political leadership, among historians at any rate, increased with the union of the crowns in 1603, and still more with the Treaty of Union in 1707. While historians and other writers differed considerably in their conclusions, Allan convincingly shows that the terms of the debate never changed radically from its origin in the Reformation. Adam Smith's concept of the "hidden hand" as a regulator of market forces, for instance, had more in common with Calvinist doctrines about Providence than current ideas about economics from right-wing politicians. David Hume himself valued historians above philosophers, and made this significant observation in an essay entitled 'Of the Study of History', addressed to "female readers": "I think it a remark worthy the attention of the speculative, that the historians have been, almost without exception, the true friends of virtue, and have always represented it in its proper colours, however they may have erred in their judgements of particular persons." Allan's book forces us to think again about the Scottish Enlightenment, and no historian can ask for higher praise than that.

Ralph Stewart's edition of James Kirkton's *History of the Church of Scotland*, written in 1693 but first published in 1817 as *The Secret History of the Church of Scotland*, has appeared just at the right time. Kirkton, a lively Presbyterian historian, is one of the many minor, but essential, figures who appear in Allan's book. Kirkton's *History* is undoubtedly a partisan work, but it served as an important source for Walter Scott's *Old Mortality*, and his style is often sardonic and wry. About what the Episcopalian-dominated Scottish authorities of the day proclaimed as an "indulgence" towards Presbyterians, for example, he has this to say: "Mr. John Vernon they kept in irons at bread and water till his leg gangren'd, which cost him his life. This was thought ane ugly shaddow of ane indulgence."

Aylwyn Clark's *An Enlightened Scot* is a biography of Hugh Cleghorn, academic and servant of the British state, who lived at the zenith of the Scottish Enlightenment. In an illuminating foreword to the book, Nicholas Phillipson observes that "Cleghorn's career was useful rather than glorious", calling him "a decent if unoriginal university teacher" and "a competent civil servant who eventually found himself out of his depth in India and Ceylon, strategically very important to the British Empire." Like his patron, the "enlightened despot" Henry Dundas, however, Cleghorn ended this phase of his career in disgrace for alleged corruption. Clark makes it evident that Cleghorn was outmanoeuvred and deceived by his bureaucratic enemy, Lord North, over pearl fisheries. A true child of the Enlightenment, Cleghorn taught civil history at St Andrews, and was a rather more broad-minded and cosmopolitan figure than Kirkton. Despite his contribution to empire-building, he was also, according to Phillipson, something of a radical republican. He therefore at least had the search for an ideal society in common with Kirkton. Kirkton believed an ideal society emerged when the Covenanters gained the upper hand in 1649–1650. He called that moment "Scotland's high noon", which takes us back to Hegel and Minerva's owl.

Mario Relich

The New Inglish–Scots Dictionar

The Concise English–Scots Dictionary, Ed Iseabail Macleod & Pauline Cairns, The Scottish National Dictionary Association/Chambers Harrap, £12.99

Traditionally, lexicographical work on the Scots language has been almost entirely descriptive, and the spellings given for Scots words have usually been based on what has been assumed to be those most popular in writing. Earlier dictionaries have carefully avoided prescribing sensible spellings for which there are few precedents and have been almost devoid of attempts at language planning. This is an essentially sterile antiquarian position. Thus the Royal Scottish Museum might seem all too suitable a setting for last October's launch of the new *Concise English–Scots Dictionary*. The ten volumes of the Scottish National Dictionary have sometimes been described as the great tombstones of the Scots language. But the new dictionary is unusual in that the editors have not been content with a solely descriptive approach to the problem of how to spell Scots words – they have had the audacity to propose a few sensible reforms to Scots orthography. This approach is more consistent with a view of Scots as a living tradition, rather than a relic from the past.

A recommendation to drop apostrophes introduced into Scots words to indicate imagined missing English letters (eg *awa* rather than *awa'*) was made both in the Scots Style Sheet, agreed at a meeting of the Makars' Club in 1947, and in the Scots Language Society (SLS) Recommendations for Writers in Scots (1985). This has now been confirmed in this work. However, no reference is made to these consensus documents. Sensible proposals for forming endings for Scots verbs that are more or less the same as in the SLS Recommendations are also given.

The general use of -ie rather than -y at the end of words (as in *bonnie*, *cannie*) is another useful step in the direction of regularising Scots orthography. The use of spellings like *bul*, *ful*, *pul* for the Scots equivalents of bull, full, pull is a good piece of language planning which indicates that the Scots pronunciation of these words is different from the English. However, to be consistent, the verb *wull* should surely be *wul*, and there are precedents for *sal* for *sall*.

On the negative side, there has been a backward move away from the native Scots digraph *ou* in favour of the English *oo*. Words like *goun*, *loun*, *toun*, which are spelt this way in the Scottish National Dictonary, now appear as *goon*, *loon*, *toon*. These spellings can lead to confusion with English words. Nor does it make much sense to use traditional spellings like *dour* and *stour*, along with *cloor* for *clour*. The spellings *dook* and *jouk* are also in conflict. The argument presented for using *roup* for *rowp*, while *cowp* is accepted for this sound, is difficult to follow, if it can be followed at all. And there's certainly something to be said for Sir Walter Scott's use of *himsell*, which indicates the stress on the final syllable, rather than *himsel*, the spelling which is given in this dictionary.

Despite these criticisms, the editors deserve great credit for this important work for the Scots language, and they give full credit for the use of William Graham's English/Scots word list, which provided a valuable foundation. Willie Graham, who died recently on holiday in the south of England, is away now, but his work is always with us. This dictionary is an important milestone for the language, and its general influence on Scots orthography should be useful. As a rule, only one or two spellings are given for each Scots word and any move away from the present state of affairs, where writers can choose from four or five possible spellings in dictionaries for some Scots words, is welcome. For those who care to search, a Scots word can be found for most English words, but the best word does not always come easily to mind: for example, the Scots word for chaos. This dictionary will make it easier for writers whose Scots is rusty to find the words they want, and it will also be invaluable for the teaching of Scots in schools and universities.

Unfortunately, there are several useful Scots words which are conspicuous by their absence. To mention two, the important verb *ti drak*, meaning to absorb, and *foraye*, meaning forever, are missed out. But no doubt this pioneer version will be succeeded by a family of more comprehensive editions. *David Purves*

Theatre Roundup

Whenever a new director is installed at the head of one of our touring companies or building-based theatres, he or she invariably sets out with lavish promises, exuberant claims and exciting plans: there will be, we are told, new plays, new audiences, productive new collaborations and plenty of challenging new work... So much for the enthusiasm of a fresh face in a new job. The reality of budgets and bank balances, production schedules and audience tastes, means that theoretical ideas often remain just that. Above all, change in the theatre takes time. You can't afford, for example, to programme a new play without giving the writer at least a year to come up with the script. To be sure of a *good* play, you're best to leave aside another year on top of that. And it's no good saying you're going to revolutionise your theatre's output over night, if the subscription audience has already bought into next autumn's season.

So although over the past two years there have been a number of changes in key directorial posts in Scottish theatre, bringing the majority of them into Scottish hands, even for the oldest of those appointments it is still early days to make definitive pronouncements about how well those directors have lived up to their initial aims. It would certainly be rash, for example, to comment on the success of Eve Jamieson at the helm of Winged Horse Touring Company on the strength of only three productions in her first sixteen months. And even after a much more productive eighteen months at Dundee Rep, Jamieson's predecessor, Hamish Glen, is only now starting to feel that he might have the measure of the tastes of local audiences and the first signs that he can lead them into previously unexplored areas.

Glen currently seems to be the director making the most headway in shaking things up. In particular he has been highly active in setting up co-productions with other companies, something which has the potential triple benefit of increasing resources for, and therefore quality of, an individual production; allowing Dundee audiences a chance to see work from outside; and spreading the name, fame and reputation of Dundee Rep about the country. For these kind of reasons as well as the opportunity to give a show a longer life, directors have frequently been known to talk about co-productions, but only now do they seem to be making them happen on any significant scale. The most successful recent example was the Tron/Dundee Rep *Macbeth*, starring Glen's brother Iain, which was the hot ticket last Mayfest before going on to sell-out houses in Dundee and might yet be revived later this year. The forthcoming adaptation of Steinbeck's *The Grapes of Wrath* is driven by the artistic resources of 7:84 (Iain Reekie is the director) but backed by financial and administrative support from Dundee Rep – there is no way otherwise that 7:84 could raise the funding for a cast of sixteen. Later in the year Glen will be swapping shows with the Royal Lyceum's Kenny Ireland, himself an advocate of increased co-operation and resource-sharing.

Ireland has been in charge of the Royal Lyceum for less than a year and although he's made some significant upheavals in that time, it is still too soon to judge the overall results. On the one hand the plays that he has put on have had varied critical success (although audiences have tended to be more enthusiastic than reviewers); *A Midsummer Night's Dream* had pace and Andy Gray on its side, but was a mish-mash of styles and poor articulation otherwise; *The Recruiting Officer* had a clumsy set, more clumsy articulation and wasn't funny; and *Gaslight* might have been best left alone. On the other hand, who else but Kenny Ireland would have thought to ask Brian Cox to star in *The Master Builder*, to get Maureen Lipman to make her directorial debut with *The Sunshine Boys*, to buy in the Tron's successful panto from the year before and to run a summer season of three plays with the same company in repertoire? I don't think the success of these individual shows matters so much as the fact that they were allowed to happen, that Ireland looked like he was preparing the ground to let great drama take root and flourish. I don't think that has happened yet, though perhaps it came close with *The Master Builder*, but the potential is there and it really is still very early days.

Younger still is the reign of Andrew McKinnon who had the unenviable task of succeeding the 25-year reign of Joan Knight at Perth Theatre. Unfortunately, the only show I have seen of his is an unremarkable *Blithe Spirit*, which I take to be unrepresentative of his debut season. More than any other director in Scotland, indeed the whole of Britain, McKinnon has to be conscious of his theatre's subscribers. There are currently around 4,000 of them (McKinnon's arrival has not prompted a mass desertion – the number has never exceeded 5,000) and while they don't exactly dictate the programming, they'd soon let it be known if the theatre didn't provide what they wanted. *Blithe Spirit* might be what you'd expect a cosy mainstream theatre like Perth to put on (which is not necessarily a bad thing), but there are examples already of more adventurous programming by McKinnon. His first season opened with the unexpected *Grand Magic*, Chris Hannan's *Elizabeth Gordon Quinn* is coming soon, and he has picked up on a couple of recent Traverse shows that might otherwise have been forgotten – Ann Marie di Mambro's *Tally's Blood* apparently transferred well, even if audiences were more resistant to Michel Tremblay's *The House Among the Stars*. It is to be hoped that the subscribers will stick with him as he programmes good strong plays that are not always the predictable choice.

Robin Peoples has been at Musselburgh's Brunton Theatre for nearly two years now and although the standard of his work is unpredictable, he looks to be doing a fair job of running an under-funded out-of-town rep with a degree of artistic credibility. Just looking across his autumn season shows – Tony Roper's *The Steamie*, John Steinbeck's *Of Mice and Men*, Willy Russell's *Educating Rita* – you can see a shrewd approach that permits the popular without being populist and lets in big themes – the decline of community spirit, the bonds of friendship, the weaknesses of the education system – without being elitist. And a considerable coup is his forthcoming premiere of the concluding part of Hector MacMillan's trilogy that began with *The Sash* and *The Funeral*. It would be nice if every theatre was able to develop and produce new work on a regular basis.

On the touring circuit, Iain Reekie has been with 7:84 for nearly two years and I feel has still to establish a clear identity for the company now that up-front politics are no longer *de rigeur*. As ever, this will take time and I like to think that Reekie has the will and imagination eventually to reassert the company as a distinctive force. So far his mixture of new, recent and classic dramas has been hit and miss, usually suggesting some kind of intelligence at work, but not yet living up to the promise of his post-student pre-7:84 work. Perhaps the increased scale and ambition of *The Grapes of Wrath* will enable him to cut out a stronger image for himself.

And finally to TAG, where Tony Graham has an unfair advantage over the directors above for having been an in-house successor to Alan Lyddiard – he took over two years ago but has been with the company since 1989. Even so, the development in his style, an eclectic melange of music, dance and performance, has been the most marked of any recent director and the accomplishment of *A Scots Quair* (reviewed last issue) should not be underestimated. That ambitious trilogy followed similar experiments such as a staging of Edwin Morgan's *From Glasgow to Saturn* poems and the kind of behind-closed-doors developmental workshops that could hold the real key to advances in the quality of our theatre.

There's still time for the current batch of artistic directors to be defeated by the tyranny of market forces, but early signs suggest that not only do we have a group of men (and I am ashamed to point out that nearly all of them are men) with strong and productive ideas, but also men with the will and energy to make those ideas actually happen. *Mark Fisher*

Pamphleteer

Rebel Inc has produced another three titles in their Rebel 100 series (they've reached No. 8). The two women writers Kim Oliver and Alison Kermack – billed as the 'younger Tom Leonard' – fare better on the whole than Paul Reekie the token male in this tranche of Rebel Lit. Alison Kermack, in *Writing Like a Bastard,* has real talent for observing and commenting on the grey schemes which litter central Scotland, as in 'IKARISS': "it wiz hardur tay buleev in/ upwurd mubility/ when that pit barbed wire/oan toappy thi lectric fens /thit ran roon thi skeem".

In 'Time and Again' she captures the grinding effect of poverty and lack of opportunity.

> thi cloak
> oan thi waw
> sezitz timety
>
> get thi bairnz reddy
> get thi hoose tidy
> get thi messijis in
> get thi tee can
> get inty bed
> an gee um hiz conjuggles
>
> thur wizza time when
> I
>
> naw thur wizny

The collection is uneven but with enough gems within to make Kermack someone to keep an eye on in the future. It's wonderful to come across another writer unashamed of her language.

Middle Aged Schoolgirl Skiving by Kim Oliver wobbles between the genuinely bad and good "When you left/ the house grew peaceful/ and a Latin American melody/ emptied itself/ out of the kitchen... The TV stayed off and all the fleas died/ in your absence." to 'Ice Ice Baby' where words have been used more because they are there rather than to communicate – the existence of words has always been a bad excuse for a poem. Some thing that Paul Reekie in 'Zap You're Pregnant' seems to suffer from. Titles like 'The Wren: Shipwrecked by the Laughter of the Gods (a Partially Non-Automatic Piece)' are designed to induce dread in any reviewer. However, amongst the mass of words something could be discerned – I'm not sure what but I hope Reekie finds it soon. This collection has a peek-a-boo feel about it. On the one hand waving an image or idea at the reader and then deluging it in a mass of obscurities. All Rebel Inc titles are available from 334 South Gyle Mains, Edinburgh, EH12 9ES.

Bel-Air, poems by Raymond Friel (£4, Southfields Press, 98 Gressenhall Road, London, SW18 5JQ) are altogether less gritty. "My dinner boiling in the bag,/ I work away my tie, tear up/ The plastic window CONGRATULATIONS,/ Uncork the flavour of the month/ And slump into my sofa-bed view/ Of motorways on top of motorways..." Closely and cosily observed poems of a comfortable life which are pleasant and well crafted but gently skim off your consciousness – the narrator's pressing concerns remain the narrator's.

Tom Kelly has two titles out (Here Now, 69 Wood Terrace, Jarrow, Tyne & Wear, NE32 5LU, £2 each) – *John Donne in Jarrow* and *Mocking the Afflicted*. Apart from the now-obligatory poem-about-writing-poems which almost always does not work and a permanent fixture of pamphleteer items, these are both excellent collections. From 'Winter Night':

> The old man lives alone.
> Winter nights are long
> and cold.
> No one calls.
> His family try to forget him.
> One of these nights
> he will die
> needing a shave and love.

Assured and well crafted.

Clio's Clavers by Murray G H Pittock (£1.50, Leerie Books, 8 Howard Place, Edinburgh EH3 5JZ) range widely between nature and the nature of the academy. "Matins are muttered, little bells are rung;/ Armenian ditties, four or five, are sung;/ No coughing don admits of God's foreknowledge/ Unless it gets his children into College./ We pray awhile, and heaven does its sums:/ Four hundred books, dark suits and no brown shoes –/ Five starred departments crammed into the pews." The rhyme does not always work and 'Someone Else's Elegy' teeters into MacGonagall territory – "The ferry was as filthy as the sea; In Amsterdam she lost her chastity,/ And in the hotel bed they shared a flea. She came to a bad end – Her parents were bitter;/ He was sad;/ She was the best screw/ One ever had." Warning: the typeface is mouse-sized – not for the hard of seeing.

Hellhound Memos by Barry MacSweeney (The Many Press, £3) is populated by Anne Sexton, Robert Johnson and Barry MacSweeney – he frequently mentions himself by name. I cannot decide if this is post-modernism or irritating self promotion. However he does manage to put B&Q on the literary map in between advising Anne Sexton of the whereabouts of all-night chemists. "So quiet tonight I can barely hear the brushing of an angel's wings./ So quiet and pleasant it is as if I am in B&Q./ O Darlington Susan, what pleasant times /in the Calor Gas centre at Scotch Corner..." Also published by The Many Press, *Being Here* by Amarjit Chandan (£1.95 post free from 15 Norcott Road, London, N16 7BJ) In the afterword he writes "I think, feel and dream in Punjabi. My language is my real home, my last retreat." As a member of the Maoist Naxalite movement, entailing imprisonment and two years in solitary confinement, he now lives in exile.

I came on it once, the Punjabi word *Lasan*
written up on a huge billboard
For women farm workers
In a far-flung corner of California
And I felt

My language had welcomed me
Shaken my hands
Embraced me
Wished me good luck
For a moment the taste of the word
Lasan was like
A sugar lump on my tongue

Johnstone Writers Group have produced *Now Read This*, a lively anthology of prose and poetry (£2, Available from Renfrew District Libraries). The best piece by far is the story by Jackie Whittet about the life and times of a prisoner – "I had planned tae go tae the party dressed as an SMT bus, but that wis unti I wis thrown tae the lions, Sheriff Lyons tae be precise." *Our Voices to the Wind – Poems from Shetland* by Glynda Batchelor is illustrated by the author, and is available from her at Durigarth, Dunrossness, Shetland for £3.95 including postage. The poems are steeped in Shetland. You can almost smell the salt spray; the Christian beliefs of the author also come through strongly. Well-crafted as they are, I would have like to have read more poems in the Shetland dialect. *Homage to Beltrees* by Alistair Mackinnon is a varied collection of poems, many on the theme of trees. He uses both Scots and English sometimes influenced by other poets. 'Country Kirkyaird efir Herman Hesse': "Amang moss dreepit crosses/ douce sunlicht, the reek o flooers/ and bees din/ the blesst lie snod/ agin the yirths hert./ The blesst whae have come hame,/ quietlike, tae rest/ in mithers lap". *Homage to Beltrees* is available from the author for £3 at 9 Burnside Terrace, Kilbarchan, PA10 2EY.

My favourite poem in *Mother Earth* by Nyki Blatchley is 'Little Miss Christabel Clitheroe' who dieted to get her man – "her gravity grew more/ as her size grew less/ the process was taking its toll/ till at last an event-horizon formed/ and Christabel became a black hole/ poor Clarence was pulled inside at once/ the researchers followed him through/ A PRIEST CAME TO EXORCISE HER/ Christabel swallowed him too." Available from Nyki Blatchley at Another Earth Press, 8 Hunstanton Close, Luton, Beds, LU4 9HB.

Finally:

The Female Entertainer threatened the
Young Boy –

'Eat a piece of my Muesli Cake or I'll
Arrange for my Mail to be delivered by a
Privatised Postman.' Blonk Junior made one
Last bid to escape: 'Look at what my Grannie
In Patna has given me to wear,' he gasped.
He dropped his regulation thick woollen grey
Post Office Trousers to reveal a Cotton/Lycra
Leotard coloured banana. 'I must have your
Leotard', shouted the envious Woman and they
Fought once more.

If you would like to know what happened before and after, *Oh No!* is available for £2 from Brent Hodgson, Ayrshire Writers, 61 Sorrel Drive, Ayr, KA7 3XR. It has many other ruminations on life – the job centre in Paisley, a job application sermon, and a Shakespearian sonnet for Murdo and Iain Crichton Smith, all in Hodgson's inimitable style of English and pidgin Scots.

Mary Gordon

Catalogue

The Mainstream Companion to Scottish Literature is essentially a reprint of Trevor Royle's Macmillan Companion published ten years ago, updated to include such glaring omissions as Alasdair Gray and Jessie Kesson, though there are inevitably many more on the contemporary scene tapping at the cover waiting to be let in – happily. Odd grammatical infelicities from the Macmillan are lovingly preserved and the price, £12.99, is a modest enough increase on the original's £8.95. Every home should have one, not least because it helps contextualise virtually every work of Scottish literature that may come your way.

For example, if you have never felt moved to read Thomas Carlyle, finding volumes 19–21 of *The Collected Letters of Thomas and Jane Welsh Carlyle* (Duke University/Edinburgh University Presses, ISBN 0-8223-1286-7/1287-5/1288-3), on the desk leads to the useful vignettes on the couple in the *Companion*, a context for TC's foul, bilious letter to RW Emerson dated 18 December 1846 fulminating on the Irish Question and against a range of other topics that most Scots would consider virtues. (I notice, *inter alia*, that had J Danforth Quayle read this letter, he would have been able to plead: "but Thomas Carlyle spells it 'potatoe'".) The strange thing is that a lot of the vivid, livid, taxi-driver rhetoric crashes around in the mind suggesting that he disapproves of something without it necessarily being clear exactly what it is that he thinks – only what he *doesn't* think. Jane Carlyle comes over as altogether more temperate, no mean conjuror with the words herself. It's also noticeable that, for someone of such cantankerously reactionary views, TC writes with respect for – and to – numerous women without seeming patronising, if not by today's standards, certainly by those of his time.

If, to the outsider, the task of compiling the forty-odd volumes (we're only about half-way with vols 19–21) resembles one of those jobs the Terrible Trivium lined up for Milo and his chums in *The Phantom Tolbooth*, like filling a well using an eyedropper, the joint Duke/Edinburgh University team's scholarship is indefatigably meticulous and superb. One footnote, for example, patiently points out that "upstairs, downstairs, in my lady's chamber" is a reference to the children's nursery rhyme Goosy Goosy Gander.

With James McKay's prizewinning biography, and now Prof. Donald Low's *The Songs of Robert Burns* (Routledge, gasp, £120), what treasures can we expect to see when the bicentenary of Burns' death rolls round in 1996? What makes the present volume 'definitive' (since it does not attempt to be 'complete') is the inclusion of the bawdy songs published privately in *The Merry Muses of Caledonia*. That, and a great deal of painstaking scholarship both in Scotland and in that cave of gold, the Thomas Cooper Library at the University of South Carolina. The chiefest of its virtues, this book, is that it is a sort of groyne, against which the shifting sands of fashion, driven by an ever-changing intellectual climate, can shift only so far. Not only that, but through the attention of singers, who will relish the wealth of musical material here, the book will come to life – a rare accolade.

Burns features in the early pages of *Heirs of the Enlightenment,* George Pottinger's history of the early days (1800–1830) of the Edinburgh Review (Scottish Academic Press, £15), the days when Sir Walter Scott, despising its politics, nevertheless held it to be required reading. *Spectrum of Decadence* (Routledge, £37.50) is Murray Pittock's study of British literature of the 1890s. Interestingly, Decadence seems to be defined as a hunger for 'the other' – what lies beyond accepted norms in the broadest sense.

Four magnificent fine art books from Canongate: *Glasgow Girls* (ed Jude Burkhauser, £30) is a companion volume to the exhibition, subtitled *Women in Art and Design 1880–1920*, mounted during Glasgow's year as City of Culture. Accompanying over 300 illustrations, many in full colour, is a lengthy, thoroughly-researched text which serves as a useful primer in feminist art theory quite apart from its value as cultural record. *The Enchanted World of Jessie M King* by Colin White (£16.95) focuses on one of the most prominent of the 'Glasgow Girls', achieving what one might describe as an accidental deconstruction of King's world, written as it is from a rather more traditional critical perspective. *Explorations in Wood* (Giles Sutherland, £25), also published to coincide with an exhibition, this time in the Royal Botanic Gardens, looks at the work of Tim Stead, sculptor and furniture-maker, whose sympathy with his chosen material makes me wonder whether it is sap that flows in his veins. *Alberto Morrocco* (Victoria Keller & Clara Young, £14.99) is a warm and generous tribute to one of Scotland's most distinguished and influential artists, published to coincide with the major retrospective mounted in Dundee to mark his 75th birthday last year.

Speaking of Dundee, where Morrocco taught for many years, there has been a noticeable swelling of civic pride there over recent years: the city's distinctive personality is explored in *The Life and Times of Dundee* (Christopher Whatley, David Swinfen & Annette Smith, John Donald, £9.95) with a nice balance of historical scruple and human warmth. On a broader canvas, Andrew Marr's *The Battle for Scotland* (Penguin, £5.99) is a lucid review of Scotland's struggle for self-determination this century. Judging from the behaviour of politicians on all sides Marr records in painful detail, the book might better be called the Squabble for Scotland.

Remaining in the historical arena, WH McDowell's *History of BBC Broadcasting in Scotland 1923–1983* (EUP, £45) is a surprisingly dull book, without a single illustration, a patrician reeling-off of committees and boards and societies as though these entities had a life of their own. When individuals venture into the foreground, they tend to be mannequins rather than the cursing, spitting flesh and blood of Andrew Marr's unruly pageant. *A propos*, it's difficult to take seriously *Scotland's Constitution* (£3.95, Moffat Publishing, The Quadrangle, Ruchill St, Glasgow G20 9PX) when the articles are interspersed with hilariously inept drawings. Nevertheless, the product of seven years' work by some of Scotland's top lawyers between 1957–1964, the more serious question is whether the document is not already dated? Do the people have a say, fundamentally, on whether the putative independent Scotland should be a monarchy or a republic, for example?

The Pentland Press specialises in the kind of book that commercial publishers eschew – books of limited appeal which nevertheless have a potential readership. *The Real Paradise: Memories of Africa 1950–1963 (£24.50)* is Ann M Davidson's memoir of the dying days of British rule in Africa; *The Holy Goalie* (£12.50), an autobiography by the Very Revd R Leonard Small: one-time Amateur International at Soccer and Moderator of the General Assembly of the Church of Scotland. *Not Our Own Light* (£7.50) is a collection of metaphysical poetry by Thomas Martin, while *Years of Conflict* (£7.50) is a collection of war poetry by William E (Ted) Morris, International Poet Laureate of New Zealand.

Similar boat, different publisher, is *The Bonnie Banks* by Hugh McBain (Jordanbooks, £6.95), a wry Glaswegian view of the world of international high finance meeting the Highland Clan system, written in a likeable style not dissimilar in places to Ivor Cutler.

As the centenary of Robert Louis Stevenson's death begins, the first of many new editions to reach this office is Everyman's *Travels with a Donkey / An Inland Voyage / The Silverado Squatters* edited by Trevor Royle: well worth the £4.99. Another new edition, this time from Polygon, is *Stained Radiance* by J Leslie Mitchell (£7.95). *C'est a dire*, the first novel of Lewis Grassic Gibbon, written in a lively, brittle, clipped language capturing with great assurance the tangy, adventuresome flavour of being a Scot abroad in 1920s London.

A big enough hit on the '92 Edinburgh Fringe to leave a crater, lively is the word, too, for Edwin Morgan's brilliant adaptation into Scots verse of Rostand's *Cyrano de Bergerac* (Carcanet, £6.95). Last year's Scots triumph on the Fringe was *Klytemnestra's Bairns*, Bill Dunlop's adaptation of Aeschylus, published by Diehard at £4.50. A welcome trickle of new Scots theatre in print is building up.

Something else that has flourished over the years is the Eastern European connection, fostered by the Department of Slavonic Studies at Glasgow University as much as by individual contacts by writers from MacDiarmid on. To mark the occasion of his retirement in 1991, *The Wider Europe: Essays on Slavonic Languages and Cultures* (Astra Press) honours Professor Peter Henry with diverse and absorbing essays on a variety of topics from 18th century translation of Chinese characters, to Lumir Soukup on the Muirs. The same range of fascinating material can be found in *Scotland and the Slavs*, Selected Papers from the Glasgow-90 East–West Forum edited by Peter Henry, Jim MacDonald and Halina Moss, also from Astra Press; and in *Coexistence*, an international affairs magazine published by Martinus Nijhoff, ISSN 0587-5994, of which Vol 29/2 is guest-edited by Peter Henry. Among the latter's wide range of items is an interesting piece by Rory Watson, 'Dostoevsky, Bakhtin, MacDiarmid and the Dooble Tongue', dialogics, Menippean satire *et cetera*. So, it seems safe to say, Bakhtin's bakhtin fashion. Hahahahaha!

Notes on Contributors

Alison Armstrong's stories have appeared in a number of Scottish magazines and collections. She lives near Alloa with six goldfish, two parakeets and a fiance.

Marion Arnott: member of Paisley Writer's Group. Work has not appeared in places too numerous to mention, but in *Scottish Child* and *West Coast* magazine.

Annette Berman: Stirling-based writer and Art Teacher. Winner of the Hugh McDiarmid Trophy in the 1991 Scottish International Open Poetry Competition.

Peter Cudmore: assistant editor, *Chapman*. Musical background includes composition classes with Peter Maxwell Davies back in the '70s when he wasn't called Sir; currently fully occupied with writing.

Jenni Daiches: In charge of publications for the National Museums of Scotland, as well as a distinguished RLS scholar and authority on Naomi Mitchison.

Christine De Luca: Born Shetland, now living in Edinburgh. Ex-teacher, now educational researcher. Has been writing in English and Shetland dialect, on and off, for 5 years.

Mark Fisher: Managing editor of *Theatre Scotland* and theatre editor of *The List*.

Valerie Gillies: Writer in residence, Mid/East Lothian. Work in multi-media exhibition *River Spirits*, with two visual artists and fellow-poet Harvey Holton, recently shown at Dundee's McManus Galleries.

Leslie Hills is an independent television producer. She was a member of Engender's Interim Board until December 1993.

Jane Humphries: freelance writer now working for Waterstone's in Dublin.

Kathleen Jones born and brought up on hill farms in the Lake District & Scottish Borders. Now lives in Cumbria and makes a precarious living from biography, fiction and poetry.

Margaret Macaulay works in an Edinburgh bookshop. Previously journalist, housewife, and schoolteacher. Latest excuse for not getting down to writing? Being Lachlan's granny.

Ann McKay: Now a staff music producer at BBC Glasgow, was until recently Director of the Scottish Music Information Centre.

Catriona Montgomery: born Skye, 1947; her new collection of poetry, *Re Na H-Oidhche* has just been published by Canongate.

Honor Patching: Born Brighton, now living in the East Neuk of Fife. Poetry & prose published in *Original Prints 4*, *London Magazine*, *Outposts* and *The Common Thread*.

Sylvia Pearson: Lives in Edinburgh, stories in Polygon's *Original Prints IV*, HarperCollins Short Story Anthologies 1993 & 1994.

David Purves: Born Selkirk, now lives in Edinburgh. Author of poems, plays and translations in Scots. Editor of *Lallans* and past Presis of the Scots Language Society.

Mario Relich is a contributor to the *Oxford Companion to Twentieth Century Poetry*, edited by Ian Hamilton.

Lydia Robb: Poetry and prose in various anthologies. Past winner of the SLS McLellan Tassie 1987 and MacDiarmid Tassie 1992.

Jenny Robertson: rooted in Scotland, lives in St Petersburg. Two collections of poetry, books for children and adults published, currently writing novel on Polish/Jewish themes.

Roberta ShoafEnge: born somewhere in the USA, now lives in Glasgow and teaches mime; MPhil in Modern Poetry from Stirling University (inexplicably, the course has since been dropped).

Morelle Smith: writes poetry, fiction and articles, published in various magazines and anthologies. Has had numerous occupations, including artist's model, house-painter, astrologer and teacher.

Valerie Thornton writes poems, short stories and articles. She is a creative writing tutor, currently editing a book to teach creative writing skills to school pupils and students.

Sheena Wellington: Singer, broadcaster, tireless worker for the traditional arts in Scotland. Tapes available, including *Clearsang*.

Fiona Wilson is a poet and essyist currently resident in New York. Her work has most recently appeared in *Oxford Poetry*, *Verse* and *New Writing Scotland 10*.

Apologies to Janice Galloway for the errors in her biographical note in the last issue. It should have read: born Ayrshire, currently working as writer in residence at four Scottish prisons and at home rearing James. New novel, *Foreign Parts* due from Jonathan Cape in April 1994.

Apologies too to Tessa Ransford for the gremlin that let an uncorrected version of her poems into print. We will be republishing 'Golden Images' in the next issue – PC